Mental
Maths
in Minutes

for ages 9–11

Maths Minutes

Maths Minutes provide a clear, brisk, enjoyable start to the daily maths lesson. They are quick and easy to administer, each one lasting one minute. They allow each child to progress at their own pace, hence providing in-built differentiation. Marking is also quick and easy. In effect the daily maths minute does for mental calculation what daily reading does for reading fluency and development. In addition to their work in class, pupils can be allowed to take their 'minutes' home for practice. In this way parents are aware of the progress of their children.

Each photocopied sheet contains either three or four Maths Minute strips. Each pupil is given one strip (face down). The strips are given out randomly within a level. When all pupils have their strips they are told to begin. They complete as many calculations as they can within the one minute time limit. Within the first few days, some pupils will be progressing to a new level of work while others will still be practising effectively at the first level. After a few weeks, the teacher may be distributing strips at a variety of levels.

At this point storage of the strips can become difficult! We suggest that the three or four strips for each Maths Minute are clipped together randomly. At the start of the session each pupil is given a strip at random from their appropriate Maths Minute. They may have had the same strip before but this does not matter.

Each of the strips on the first twenty Maths Minutes has 24 calculations. To progress from one level to the next a pupil must attain 20 or more correct answers on three consecutive occasions. Maths Minutes 21 to 30 have 20 questions on each strip and we suggest a target of 15 correct answers in one minute. Maths Minutes 31 to 35 have 16 questions per strip and we suggest a target of 12 correct in one minute. Maths Minutes 36 to 39 have just 12 questions on each strip with a target of 9 correct.

These Maths Minutes are so quick and easy to administer that there is time for a teacher to incorporate these into the daily numeracy lesson in addition to a variety of other oral and mental work. Whilst the questions on each strip appear to be random, within them there are some clusters of related calculations that include number patterns which aid understanding. These also provide teaching points for group and class work.

Andrew Brodie Publications
© A & C Black Publishers Ltd.

How to use Maths Minutes.

✳ This guide gives one way to use Maths Minutes. You may wish to modify the way you use this book to best suit the group of children with whom you are working.

✳ Distribute a Maths Minute strip (at the appropriate level/levels) face down to each pupil - remember to ask them to write their name on it!

✳ All pupils turn over their Maths Minute strips and begin, on your signal.

✳ All pupils must stop after one minute, again on your signal.

✳ Maths Minute strips are collected ready for marking.

✳ The completed strips are very quickly and easily marked by an appropriate classroom adult using the answer sheets provided.

✳ We suggest that you use a page of an exercise book for each pupil. Write down the number of the Maths Minute that you have chosen as the child's first level. Enter the pupil's mark each day.

✳ Marks reaching or exceeding the number needed for progressing to the next level can simply be marked with a 'blot' or blob' near the score. e.g. 23 ●

✳ When a pupil has completed three consecutive 'blobby' scores they are considered ready to progress to the following level.

✳ It may be found useful to encourage pupils to take home their completed Maths Minute strips, hence promoting home-school maths links. It is easy to then cut the answers off the completed strip - place it on a sheet of plain paper and see if they have improved from the day before or use it as a practice strip.

✳ In use it has been found that many pupils are keen to have a whole sheet of all 4 strips to prepare for the level they are approaching, i.e. on completing Maths Minute 3 they may ask for a Maths Minute 4 sheet of strips to take away and practise.

✳ It is important that each pupil is aiming each day to achieve their own personal best score and is not in competition with other pupils. For this reason we do not advocate any type of wall record chart showing whole class achievements.

✳ The Maths Minute strips are extremely valuable in helping teachers spot particular mathematical difficulties an individual pupil may have. This of course allows these learning issues to be dealt with at an early stage.

✳ Some pupils may complete any particular level very quickly whilst others could take several weeks.

Andrew Brodie Publications
© A & C Black Publishers Ltd.

Contents

◆ Name	● Name	▲ Name	✳ Name
Round these numbers to the nearest 10	Round these numbers to the nearest 10	Round these numbers to the nearest 10	Round these numbers to the nearest 10
27 ➡	37 ➡	49 ➡	67 ➡
17 ➡	17 ➡	14 ➡	19 ➡
93 ➡	14 ➡	45 ➡	54 ➡
85 ➡	25 ➡	15 ➡	26 ➡
21 ➡	39 ➡	11 ➡	18 ➡
68 ➡	59 ➡	78 ➡	31 ➡
33 ➡	81 ➡	79 ➡	99 ➡
46 ➡	75 ➡	76 ➡	47 ➡
72 ➡	62 ➡	41 ➡	59 ➡
54 ➡	31 ➡	83 ➡	81 ➡
99 ➡	81 ➡	99 ➡	62 ➡
37 ➡	86 ➡	63 ➡	79 ➡
156 ➡	48 ➡	899 ➡	765 ➡
911 ➡	125 ➡	777 ➡	767 ➡
315 ➡	971 ➡	638 ➡	768 ➡
273 ➡	381 ➡	964 ➡	921 ➡
192 ➡	249 ➡	199 ➡	153 ➡
438 ➡	599 ➡	119 ➡	899 ➡
845 ➡	478 ➡	255 ➡	289 ➡
958 ➡	399 ➡	64 ➡	378 ➡
587 ➡	612 ➡	333 ➡	511 ➡
416 ➡	933 ➡	522 ➡	433 ➡
625 ➡	475 ➡	579 ➡	621 ➡
736 ➡	884 ➡	481 ➡	768 ➡

Maths Minute 1   **Maths Minute 1**   **Maths Minute 1**   **Maths Minute 1**

Andrew Brodie Publications   Andrew Brodie Publications   Andrew Brodie Publications   Andrew Brodie Publications

◆ ANSWERS

Round these numbers to the nearest 10

27	➡	30
17	➡	20
93	➡	90
85	➡	90
21	➡	20
68	➡	70
33	➡	30
46	➡	50
72	➡	70
54	➡	50
99	➡	100
37	➡	40
156	➡	160
911	➡	910
315	➡	320
273	➡	270
192	➡	190
438	➡	440
845	➡	850
958	➡	960
587	➡	590
416	➡	420
625	➡	630
736	➡	740

ANSWERS

Maths Minute 1

Andrew Brodie Publications
© A & C Black Publishers Ltd.

● ANSWERS

Round these numbers to the nearest 10

37	➡	40
17	➡	20
14	➡	10
25	➡	30
39	➡	40
59	➡	60
81	➡	80
75	➡	80
62	➡	60
31	➡	30
81	➡	80
86	➡	90
48	➡	50
125	➡	130
971	➡	970
381	➡	380
249	➡	250
599	➡	600
478	➡	480
399	➡	400
612	➡	610
933	➡	930
475	➡	480
884	➡	880

ANSWERS

Maths Minute 1

Andrew Brodie Publications
© A & C Black Publishers Ltd.

▲ ANSWERS

Round these numbers to the nearest 10

49	➡	50
14	➡	10
45	➡	50
15	➡	20
11	➡	10
78	➡	80
79	➡	80
76	➡	80
41	➡	40
83	➡	80
99	➡	100
63	➡	60
899	➡	900
777	➡	780
638	➡	640
964	➡	960
199	➡	200
119	➡	120
255	➡	260
64	➡	60
333	➡	330
522	➡	520
579	➡	580
481	➡	480

ANSWERS

Maths Minute 1

Andrew Brodie Publications
© A & C Black Publishers Ltd.

✸ ANSWERS

Round these numbers to the nearest 10

67	➡	70
19	➡	20
54	➡	50
26	➡	30
18	➡	20
31	➡	30
99	➡	100
47	➡	50
59	➡	60
81	➡	80
62	➡	60
79	➡	80
765	➡	770
767	➡	770
768	➡	770
921	➡	920
153	➡	150
899	➡	900
289	➡	290
378	➡	380
511	➡	510
433	➡	430
621	➡	620
768	➡	770

ANSWERS

Maths Minute 1

Andrew Brodie Publications
© A & C Black Publishers Ltd.

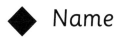 Name　　　 Name　　　▲ Name　　　 Name

Finding fractional parts	Finding fractional parts	Finding fractional parts	Finding fractional parts
$\frac{1}{2}$ of 8 =	$\frac{1}{2}$ of 2 =	$\frac{1}{2}$ of 10 =	$\frac{1}{2}$ of 10 =
$\frac{1}{2}$ of 6 =	$\frac{1}{2}$ of 4 =	$\frac{1}{2}$ of 14 =	$\frac{1}{3}$ of 30 =
$\frac{1}{2}$ of 20 =	$\frac{1}{2}$ of 22 =	$\frac{1}{2}$ of 24 =	$\frac{1}{4}$ of 80 =
$\frac{1}{2}$ of 24 =	$\frac{1}{2}$ of 36 =	$\frac{1}{2}$ of 44 =	$\frac{1}{10}$ of 80 =
$\frac{1}{2}$ of 50 =	$\frac{1}{2}$ of 60 =	$\frac{1}{2}$ of 144 =	$\frac{1}{2}$ of 80 =
$\frac{1}{2}$ of 26 =	$\frac{1}{2}$ of 50 =	$\frac{1}{2}$ of 150 =	$\frac{1}{2}$ of 36 =
$\frac{1}{2}$ of 88 =	$\frac{1}{2}$ of 54 =	$\frac{1}{2}$ of 90 =	$\frac{1}{4}$ of 36 =
$\frac{1}{2}$ of 100 =	$\frac{1}{2}$ of 64 =	$\frac{1}{2}$ of 70 =	$\frac{1}{3}$ of 36 =
$\frac{1}{2}$ of 36 =	$\frac{1}{2}$ of 18 =	$\frac{1}{2}$ of 76 =	$\frac{1}{2}$ of 60 =
$\frac{1}{4}$ of 8 =	$\frac{1}{4}$ of 4 =	$\frac{1}{4}$ of 12 =	$\frac{1}{3}$ of 60 =
$\frac{1}{4}$ of 100 =	$\frac{1}{4}$ of 200 =	$\frac{1}{4}$ of 400 =	$\frac{1}{4}$ of 60 =
$\frac{1}{4}$ of 16 =	$\frac{1}{4}$ of 24 =	$\frac{1}{4}$ of 28 =	$\frac{1}{10}$ of 60 =
$\frac{1}{4}$ of 20 =	$\frac{1}{4}$ of 40 =	$\frac{1}{4}$ of 44 =	$\frac{1}{2}$ of 100 =
$\frac{1}{3}$ of 9 =	$\frac{1}{3}$ of 3 =	$\frac{1}{3}$ of 6 =	$\frac{1}{4}$ of 100 =
$\frac{1}{3}$ of 6 =	$\frac{1}{3}$ of 12 =	$\frac{1}{3}$ of 15 =	$\frac{1}{10}$ of 100 =
$\frac{1}{3}$ of 12 =	$\frac{1}{3}$ of 24 =	$\frac{1}{3}$ of 33 =	$\frac{1}{2}$ of 124 =
$\frac{1}{3}$ of 30 =	$\frac{1}{3}$ of 60 =	$\frac{1}{3}$ of 90 =	$\frac{1}{4}$ of 124 =
$\frac{1}{10}$ of 10 =	$\frac{1}{10}$ of 100 =	$\frac{1}{10}$ of 90 =	$\frac{1}{2}$ of 4 =
$\frac{1}{10}$ of 50 =	$\frac{1}{10}$ of 250 =	$\frac{1}{10}$ of 300 =	$\frac{1}{2}$ of 40 =
$\frac{1}{10}$ of 30 =	$\frac{1}{10}$ of 360 =	$\frac{1}{10}$ of 100 =	$\frac{1}{2}$ of 400 =
$\frac{1}{10}$ of 80 =	$\frac{1}{10}$ of 70 =	$\frac{1}{10}$ of 1000 =	$\frac{1}{4}$ of 4 =
$\frac{1}{4}$ of 64 =	$\frac{1}{4}$ of 84 =	$\frac{1}{4}$ of 104 =	$\frac{1}{4}$ of 40 =
$\frac{1}{3}$ of 36 =	$\frac{1}{3}$ of 63 =	$\frac{1}{3}$ of 93 =	$\frac{1}{4}$ of 400 =
$\frac{1}{3}$ of 45 =	$\frac{1}{3}$ of 69 =	$\frac{1}{3}$ of 66 =	$\frac{1}{3}$ of 39 =

Maths Minute 2　　**Maths Minute 2**　　**Maths Minute 2**　　**Maths Minute 2**

Andrew Brodie Publications　Andrew Brodie Publications　Andrew Brodie Publications　Andrew Brodie Publications
© A & C Black Publishers Ltd.　© A & C Black Publishers Ltd.　© A & C Black Publishers Ltd.　© A & C Black Publishers Ltd.

 **ANSWERS**

Finding fractional parts

$\frac{1}{2}$ of 8 =	4
$\frac{1}{2}$ of 6 =	3
$\frac{1}{2}$ of 20 =	10
$\frac{1}{2}$ of 24 =	12
$\frac{1}{2}$ of 50 =	25
$\frac{1}{2}$ of 26 =	13
$\frac{1}{2}$ of 88 =	44
$\frac{1}{2}$ of 100 =	50
$\frac{1}{2}$ of 36 =	18
$\frac{1}{4}$ of 8 =	2
$\frac{1}{4}$ of 100 =	25
$\frac{1}{4}$ of 16 =	4
$\frac{1}{4}$ of 20 =	5
$\frac{1}{3}$ of 9 =	3
$\frac{1}{3}$ of 6 =	2
$\frac{1}{3}$ of 12 =	4
$\frac{1}{3}$ of 30 =	10
$\frac{1}{10}$ of 10 =	1
$\frac{1}{10}$ of 50 =	5
$\frac{1}{10}$ of 30 =	3
$\frac{1}{10}$ of 80 =	8
$\frac{1}{4}$ of 64 =	16
$\frac{1}{3}$ of 36 =	12
$\frac{1}{3}$ of 45 =	15

ANSWERS

Maths Minute 2

Andrew Brodie Publications
© A & C Black Publishers Ltd.

● **ANSWERS**

Finding fractional parts

$\frac{1}{2}$ of 2 =	1
$\frac{1}{2}$ of 4 =	2
$\frac{1}{2}$ of 22 =	11
$\frac{1}{2}$ of 36 =	18
$\frac{1}{2}$ of 60 =	30
$\frac{1}{2}$ of 50 =	25
$\frac{1}{2}$ of 54 =	27
$\frac{1}{2}$ of 64 =	32
$\frac{1}{2}$ of 18 =	9
$\frac{1}{4}$ of 4 =	1
$\frac{1}{4}$ of 200 =	50
$\frac{1}{4}$ of 24 =	6
$\frac{1}{4}$ of 40 =	10
$\frac{1}{3}$ of 3 =	1
$\frac{1}{3}$ of 12 =	4
$\frac{1}{3}$ of 24 =	8
$\frac{1}{3}$ of 60 =	20
$\frac{1}{10}$ of 100 =	10
$\frac{1}{10}$ of 250 =	25
$\frac{1}{10}$ of 360 =	36
$\frac{1}{10}$ of 70 =	7
$\frac{1}{4}$ of 84 =	21
$\frac{1}{3}$ of 63 =	21
$\frac{1}{3}$ of 69 =	23

ANSWERS

Maths Minute 2

Andrew Brodie Publications
© A & C Black Publishers Ltd.

▲ **ANSWERS**

Finding fractional parts

$\frac{1}{2}$ of 10 =	5
$\frac{1}{2}$ of 14 =	7
$\frac{1}{2}$ of 24 =	12
$\frac{1}{2}$ of 44 =	22
$\frac{1}{2}$ of 144 =	72
$\frac{1}{2}$ of 150 =	75
$\frac{1}{2}$ of 90 =	45
$\frac{1}{2}$ of 70 =	35
$\frac{1}{2}$ of 76 =	38
$\frac{1}{4}$ of 12 =	3
$\frac{1}{4}$ of 400 =	100
$\frac{1}{4}$ of 28 =	7
$\frac{1}{4}$ of 44 =	11
$\frac{1}{3}$ of 6 =	2
$\frac{1}{3}$ of 15 =	5
$\frac{1}{3}$ of 33 =	11
$\frac{1}{3}$ of 90 =	30
$\frac{1}{10}$ of 90 =	9
$\frac{1}{10}$ of 300 =	30
$\frac{1}{10}$ of 100 =	10
$\frac{1}{10}$ of 1000 =	100
$\frac{1}{4}$ of 104 =	26
$\frac{1}{3}$ of 93 =	31
$\frac{1}{3}$ of 66 =	22

ANSWERS

Maths Minute 2

Andrew Brodie Publications
© A & C Black Publishers Ltd.

 **ANSWERS**

Finding fractional parts

$\frac{1}{2}$ of 10 =	5
$\frac{1}{3}$ of 30 =	10
$\frac{1}{4}$ of 80 =	20
$\frac{1}{10}$ of 80 =	8
$\frac{1}{2}$ of 80 =	40
$\frac{1}{2}$ of 36 =	18
$\frac{1}{4}$ of 36 =	9
$\frac{1}{3}$ of 36 =	12
$\frac{1}{2}$ of 60 =	30
$\frac{1}{3}$ of 60 =	20
$\frac{1}{4}$ of 60 =	15
$\frac{1}{10}$ of 60 =	6
$\frac{1}{2}$ of 100 =	50
$\frac{1}{4}$ of 100 =	25
$\frac{1}{10}$ of 100 =	10
$\frac{1}{2}$ of 124 =	62
$\frac{1}{4}$ of 124 =	31
$\frac{1}{2}$ of 4 =	2
$\frac{1}{2}$ of 40 =	20
$\frac{1}{2}$ of 400 =	200
$\frac{1}{4}$ of 4 =	1
$\frac{1}{4}$ of 40 =	10
$\frac{1}{4}$ of 400 =	100
$\frac{1}{3}$ of 39 =	13

ANSWERS

Maths Minute 2

Andrew Brodie Publications
© A & C Black Publishers Ltd.

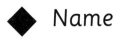 Name    Name    Name    Name

Finding fractional parts	Finding fractional parts	Finding fractional parts	Finding fractional parts
$\frac{1}{3}$ of 6 =	$\frac{1}{3}$ of 18 =	$\frac{1}{3}$ of 21 =	$\frac{1}{3}$ of 12 =
$\frac{2}{3}$ of 6 =	$\frac{2}{3}$ of 18 =	$\frac{2}{3}$ of 21 =	$\frac{2}{3}$ of 12 =
$\frac{1}{3}$ of 9 =	$\frac{1}{3}$ of 36 =	$\frac{1}{3}$ of 36 =	$\frac{1}{3}$ of 42 =
$\frac{2}{3}$ of 9 =	$\frac{2}{3}$ of 36 =	$\frac{2}{3}$ of 36 =	$\frac{2}{3}$ of 42 =
$\frac{2}{3}$ of 12 =	$\frac{2}{3}$ of 30 =	$\frac{2}{3}$ of 12 =	$\frac{2}{3}$ of 39 =
$\frac{2}{3}$ of 30 =	$\frac{2}{3}$ of 33 =	$\frac{2}{3}$ of 39 =	$\frac{2}{3}$ of 3 =
$\frac{1}{4}$ of 8 =	$\frac{1}{4}$ of 24 =	$\frac{1}{4}$ of 32 =	$\frac{1}{4}$ of 16 =
$\frac{3}{4}$ of 8 =	$\frac{3}{4}$ of 24 =	$\frac{3}{4}$ of 32 =	$\frac{3}{4}$ of 16 =
$\frac{1}{4}$ of 20 =	$\frac{1}{4}$ of 44 =	$\frac{1}{4}$ of 64 =	$\frac{1}{4}$ of 40 =
$\frac{3}{4}$ of 20 =	$\frac{3}{4}$ of 44 =	$\frac{3}{4}$ of 64 =	$\frac{3}{4}$ of 40 =
$\frac{3}{4}$ of 32 =	$\frac{3}{4}$ of 48 =	$\frac{3}{4}$ of 36 =	$\frac{3}{4}$ of 24 =
$\frac{3}{4}$ of 4 =	$\frac{3}{4}$ of 100 =	$\frac{3}{4}$ of 100 =	$\frac{3}{4}$ of 28 =
$\frac{3}{4}$ of 40 =	$\frac{3}{4}$ of 80 =	$\frac{3}{4}$ of 120 =	$\frac{3}{4}$ of 56 =
$\frac{1}{4}$ of 80 =	$\frac{1}{4}$ of 32 =	$\frac{1}{4}$ of 20 =	$\frac{1}{4}$ of 48 =
$\frac{1}{4}$ of 88 =	$\frac{1}{4}$ of 36 =	$\frac{1}{4}$ of 100 =	$\frac{1}{4}$ of 52 =
$\frac{1}{10}$ of 10 =	$\frac{1}{10}$ of 20 =	$\frac{1}{10}$ of 30 =	$\frac{1}{10}$ of 40 =
$\frac{3}{10}$ of 10 =	$\frac{3}{10}$ of 20 =	$\frac{3}{10}$ of 30 =	$\frac{3}{10}$ of 40 =
$\frac{7}{10}$ of 10 =	$\frac{7}{10}$ of 20 =	$\frac{7}{10}$ of 30 =	$\frac{7}{10}$ of 40 =
$\frac{9}{10}$ of 10 =	$\frac{9}{10}$ of 20 =	$\frac{9}{10}$ of 30 =	$\frac{9}{10}$ of 40 =
$\frac{1}{3}$ of 36 =	$\frac{1}{3}$ of 12 =	$\frac{1}{3}$ of 24 =	$\frac{1}{3}$ of 48 =
$\frac{2}{3}$ of 36 =	$\frac{2}{3}$ of 12 =	$\frac{2}{3}$ of 24 =	$\frac{2}{3}$ of 48 =
$\frac{1}{4}$ of 36 =	$\frac{1}{4}$ of 12 =	$\frac{1}{4}$ of 24 =	$\frac{1}{4}$ of 48 =
$\frac{3}{4}$ of 36 =	$\frac{3}{4}$ of 12 =	$\frac{3}{4}$ of 24 =	$\frac{3}{4}$ of 48 =
$\frac{3}{10}$ of 20 =	$\frac{3}{10}$ of 30 =	$\frac{3}{10}$ of 40 =	$\frac{3}{10}$ of 50 =

Maths Minute 3   **Maths Minute 3**   **Maths Minute 3**   **Maths Minute 3**

Andrew Brodie Publications   Andrew Brodie Publications   Andrew Brodie Publications   Andrew Brodie Publications
© A & C Black Publishers Ltd.   © A & C Black Publishers Ltd.   © A & C Black Publishers Ltd.   © A & C Black Publishers Ltd.

◆ ANSWERS
Finding fractional parts

● ANSWERS
Finding fractional parts

▲ ANSWERS
Finding fractional parts

✴ ANSWERS
Finding fractional parts

Column ◆	Column ●	Column ▲	Column ✴
$\frac{1}{3}$ of 6 = 2	$\frac{1}{3}$ of 18 = 6	$\frac{1}{3}$ of 21 = 7	$\frac{1}{3}$ of 12 = 4
$\frac{2}{3}$ of 6 = 4	$\frac{2}{3}$ of 18 = 12	$\frac{2}{3}$ of 21 = 14	$\frac{2}{3}$ of 12 = 8
$\frac{1}{3}$ of 9 = 3	$\frac{1}{3}$ of 36 = 12	$\frac{1}{3}$ of 36 = 12	$\frac{1}{3}$ of 42 = 14
$\frac{2}{3}$ of 9 = 6	$\frac{2}{3}$ of 36 = 24	$\frac{2}{3}$ of 36 = 24	$\frac{2}{3}$ of 42 = 28
$\frac{2}{3}$ of 12 = 8	$\frac{2}{3}$ of 30 = 20	$\frac{2}{3}$ of 12 = 8	$\frac{2}{3}$ of 39 = 26
$\frac{2}{3}$ of 30 = 20	$\frac{2}{3}$ of 33 = 22	$\frac{2}{3}$ of 39 = 26	$\frac{2}{3}$ of 3 = 2
$\frac{1}{4}$ of 8 = 2	$\frac{1}{4}$ of 24 = 6	$\frac{1}{4}$ of 32 = 8	$\frac{1}{4}$ of 16 = 4
$\frac{3}{4}$ of 8 = 6	$\frac{3}{4}$ of 24 = 18	$\frac{3}{4}$ of 32 = 24	$\frac{3}{4}$ of 16 = 12
$\frac{1}{4}$ of 20 = 5	$\frac{1}{4}$ of 44 = 11	$\frac{1}{4}$ of 64 = 16	$\frac{1}{4}$ of 40 = 10
$\frac{3}{4}$ of 20 = 15	$\frac{3}{4}$ of 44 = 33	$\frac{3}{4}$ of 64 = 48	$\frac{3}{4}$ of 40 = 30
$\frac{3}{4}$ of 32 = 24	$\frac{3}{4}$ of 48 = 36	$\frac{3}{4}$ of 36 = 27	$\frac{3}{4}$ of 24 = 18
$\frac{3}{4}$ of 4 = 3	$\frac{3}{4}$ of 100 = 75	$\frac{3}{4}$ of 100 = 75	$\frac{3}{4}$ of 28 = 21
$\frac{3}{4}$ of 40 = 30	$\frac{3}{4}$ of 80 = 60	$\frac{3}{4}$ of 120 = 90	$\frac{3}{4}$ of 56 = 42
$\frac{1}{4}$ of 80 = 20	$\frac{1}{4}$ of 32 = 8	$\frac{1}{4}$ of 20 = 5	$\frac{1}{4}$ of 48 = 12
$\frac{1}{4}$ of 88 = 22	$\frac{1}{4}$ of 36 = 9	$\frac{1}{4}$ of 100 = 25	$\frac{1}{4}$ of 52 = 13
$\frac{1}{10}$ of 10 = 1	$\frac{1}{10}$ of 20 = 2	$\frac{1}{10}$ of 30 = 3	$\frac{1}{10}$ of 40 = 4
$\frac{3}{10}$ of 10 = 3	$\frac{3}{10}$ of 20 = 6	$\frac{3}{10}$ of 30 = 9	$\frac{3}{10}$ of 40 = 12
$\frac{7}{10}$ of 10 = 7	$\frac{7}{10}$ of 20 = 14	$\frac{7}{10}$ of 30 = 21	$\frac{7}{10}$ of 40 = 28
$\frac{9}{10}$ of 10 = 9	$\frac{9}{10}$ of 20 = 18	$\frac{9}{10}$ of 30 = 27	$\frac{9}{10}$ of 40 = 36
$\frac{1}{3}$ of 36 = 12	$\frac{1}{3}$ of 12 = 4	$\frac{1}{3}$ of 24 = 8	$\frac{1}{3}$ of 48 = 16
$\frac{2}{3}$ of 36 = 24	$\frac{2}{3}$ of 12 = 8	$\frac{2}{3}$ of 24 = 16	$\frac{2}{3}$ of 48 = 32
$\frac{1}{4}$ of 36 = 9	$\frac{1}{4}$ of 12 = 3	$\frac{1}{4}$ of 24 = 6	$\frac{1}{4}$ of 48 = 12
$\frac{3}{4}$ of 36 = 27	$\frac{3}{4}$ of 12 = 9	$\frac{3}{4}$ of 24 = 18	$\frac{3}{4}$ of 48 = 36
$\frac{3}{10}$ of 20 = 6	$\frac{3}{10}$ of 30 = 9	$\frac{3}{10}$ of 40 = 12	$\frac{3}{10}$ of 50 = 15

ANSWERS
Maths Minute 3

ANSWERS
Maths Minute 3

ANSWERS
Maths Minute 3

ANSWERS
Maths Minute 3

Andrew Brodie Publications
© A & C Black Publishers Ltd.

Andrew Brodie Publications
© A & C Black Publishers Ltd.

Andrew Brodie Publications
© A & C Black Publishers Ltd.

Andrew Brodie Publications
© A & C Black Publishers Ltd.

◆ Name	● Name	▲ Name	✳ Name
Rounding to the nearest 100	**Rounding to the nearest 100**	**Rounding to the nearest 100**	**Rounding to the nearest 100**
281 ➡	241 ➡	397 ➡	195 ➡
659 ➡	367 ➡	316 ➡	208 ➡
823 ➡	118 ➡	425 ➡	751 ➡
741 ➡	145 ➡	899 ➡	127 ➡
397 ➡	104 ➡	912 ➡	823 ➡
555 ➡	490 ➡	262 ➡	591 ➡
212 ➡	945 ➡	150 ➡	688 ➡
639 ➡	560 ➡	903 ➡	736 ➡
821 ➡	634 ➡	779 ➡	395 ➡
810 ➡	850 ➡	842 ➡	306 ➡
201 ➡	798 ➡	565 ➡	486 ➡
785 ➡	120 ➡	673 ➡	849 ➡
376 ➡	878 ➡	128 ➡	374 ➡
666 ➡	341 ➡	475 ➡	423 ➡
523 ➡	942 ➡	926 ➡	270 ➡
430 ➡	263 ➡	861 ➡	250 ➡
850 ➡	250 ➡	299 ➡	519 ➡
706 ➡	127 ➡	850 ➡	695 ➡
142 ➡	832 ➡	324 ➡	139 ➡
690 ➡	445 ➡	369 ➡	709 ➡
250 ➡	890 ➡	705 ➡	740 ➡
559 ➡	530 ➡	610 ➡	885 ➡
398 ➡	666 ➡	429 ➡	925 ➡
421 ➡	727 ➡	555 ➡	333 ➡

Maths Minute 4

Andrew Brodie Publications
© A & C Black Publishers Ltd.

◆ ANSWERS	● ANSWERS	▲ ANSWERS	✴ ANSWERS
Rounding to the nearest 100	Rounding to the nearest 100	Rounding to the nearest 100	Rounding to the nearest 100
281 ➡ 300	241 ➡ 200	397 ➡ 400	195 ➡ 200
659 ➡ 700	367 ➡ 400	316 ➡ 300	208 ➡ 200
823 ➡ 800	118 ➡ 100	425 ➡ 400	751 ➡ 800
741 ➡ 700	145 ➡ 100	899 ➡ 900	127 ➡ 100
397 ➡ 400	104 ➡ 100	912 ➡ 900	823 ➡ 800
555 ➡ 600	490 ➡ 500	262 ➡ 300	591 ➡ 600
212 ➡ 200	945 ➡ 900	150 ➡ 200	688 ➡ 700
639 ➡ 600	560 ➡ 600	903 ➡ 900	736 ➡ 700
821 ➡ 800	634 ➡ 600	779 ➡ 800	395 ➡ 400
810 ➡ 800	850 ➡ 900	842 ➡ 800	306 ➡ 300
201 ➡ 200	798 ➡ 800	565 ➡ 600	486 ➡ 500
785 ➡ 800	120 ➡ 100	673 ➡ 700	849 ➡ 800
376 ➡ 400	878 ➡ 900	128 ➡ 100	374 ➡ 400
666 ➡ 700	341 ➡ 300	475 ➡ 500	423 ➡ 400
523 ➡ 500	942 ➡ 900	926 ➡ 900	270 ➡ 300
430 ➡ 400	263 ➡ 300	861 ➡ 900	250 ➡ 300
850 ➡ 900	250 ➡ 300	299 ➡ 300	519 ➡ 500
706 ➡ 700	127 ➡ 100	850 ➡ 900	695 ➡ 700
142 ➡ 100	832 ➡ 800	324 ➡ 300	139 ➡ 100
690 ➡ 700	445 ➡ 400	369 ➡ 400	709 ➡ 700
250 ➡ 300	890 ➡ 900	705 ➡ 700	740 ➡ 700
559 ➡ 600	530 ➡ 500	610 ➡ 600	885 ➡ 900
398 ➡ 400	666 ➡ 700	429 ➡ 400	925 ➡ 900
421 ➡ 400	727 ➡ 700	555 ➡ 600	333 ➡ 300
ANSWERS	**ANSWERS**	**ANSWERS**	**ANSWERS**
Maths Minute 4	**Maths Minute 4**	**Maths Minute 4**	**Maths Minute 4**

Andrew Brodie Publications © A & C Black Publishers Ltd.   Andrew Brodie Publications © A & C Black Publishers Ltd.   Andrew Brodie Publications © A & C Black Publishers Ltd.   Andrew Brodie Publications © A & C Black Publishers Ltd.

◆ Name	● Name	▲ Name	✴ Name
Rounding to the nearest 1000	Rounding to the nearest 1000	Rounding to the nearest 1000	Rounding to the nearest 1000
2141 ➡	2001 ➡	1948 ➡	5009 ➡
3986 ➡	4127 ➡	3954 ➡	9520 ➡
7724 ➡	6489 ➡	6155 ➡	2636 ➡
4998 ➡	9153 ➡	2681 ➡	4821 ➡
6673 ➡	1500 ➡	9797 ➡	6182 ➡
1242 ➡	6141 ➡	4279 ➡	2889 ➡
4681 ➡	4698 ➡	1686 ➡	4642 ➡
6376 ➡	7163 ➡	8123 ➡	1251 ➡
2924 ➡	5929 ➡	5500 ➡	7372 ➡
2419 ➡	8668 ➡	3614 ➡	4561 ➡
5850 ➡	2626 ➡	9219 ➡	7283 ➡
8321 ➡	7205 ➡	4562 ➡	5174 ➡
1179 ➡	4803 ➡	6369 ➡	1392 ➡
7500 ➡	8595 ➡	1580 ➡	8150 ➡
8420 ➡	1962 ➡	8852 ➡	3892 ➡
2662 ➡	7781 ➡	3117 ➡	9414 ➡
9696 ➡	5578 ➡	6777 ➡	5926 ➡
5745 ➡	8349 ➡	2832 ➡	1702 ➡
8892 ➡	3333 ➡	5340 ➡	8219 ➡
9137 ➡	6291 ➡	5489 ➡	3623 ➡
1381 ➡	7872 ➡	3721 ➡	6462 ➡
6943 ➡	3753 ➡	7819 ➡	2151 ➡
9857 ➡	5741 ➡	2015 ➡	6319 ➡
4211 ➡	9920 ➡	7213 ➡	3400 ➡

Maths Minute 5

Andrew Brodie Publications
© A & C Black Publishers Ltd.

◆ ANSWERS	● ANSWERS	▲ ANSWERS	✷ ANSWERS
Rounding to the nearest 1000	Rounding to the nearest 1000	Rounding to the nearest 1000	Rounding to the nearest 1000
2141 ➡ 2000	2001 ➡ 2000	1948 ➡ 2000	5009 ➡ 5000
3986 ➡ 4000	4127 ➡ 4000	3954 ➡ 4000	9520 ➡ 10000
7724 ➡ 8000	6489 ➡ 6000	6155 ➡ 6000	2636 ➡ 3000
4998 ➡ 5000	9153 ➡ 9000	2681 ➡ 3000	4821 ➡ 5000
6673 ➡ 7000	1500 ➡ 2000	9797 ➡ 10000	6182 ➡ 6000
1242 ➡ 1000	6141 ➡ 6000	4279 ➡ 4000	2889 ➡ 3000
4681 ➡ 5000	4698 ➡ 5000	1686 ➡ 2000	4642 ➡ 5000
6376 ➡ 6000	7163 ➡ 7000	8123 ➡ 8000	1251 ➡ 1000
2924 ➡ 3000	5929 ➡ 6000	5500 ➡ 6000	7372 ➡ 7000
2419 ➡ 2000	8668 ➡ 9000	3614 ➡ 4000	4561 ➡ 5000
5850 ➡ 6000	2626 ➡ 3000	9219 ➡ 9000	7283 ➡ 7000
8321 ➡ 8000	7205 ➡ 7000	4562 ➡ 5000	5174 ➡ 5000
1179 ➡ 1000	4803 ➡ 5000	6369 ➡ 6000	1392 ➡ 1000
7500 ➡ 8000	8595 ➡ 9000	1580 ➡ 2000	8150 ➡ 8000
8420 ➡ 8000	1962 ➡ 2000	8852 ➡ 9000	3892 ➡ 4000
2662 ➡ 3000	7781 ➡ 8000	3117 ➡ 3000	9414 ➡ 9000
9696 ➡ 10000	5578 ➡ 6000	6777 ➡ 7000	5926 ➡ 6000
5745 ➡ 6000	8349 ➡ 8000	2832 ➡ 3000	1702 ➡ 2000
8892 ➡ 9000	3333 ➡ 3000	5340 ➡ 5000	8219 ➡ 8000
9137 ➡ 9000	6291 ➡ 6000	5489 ➡ 5000	3623 ➡ 4000
1381 ➡ 1000	7872 ➡ 8000	3721 ➡ 4000	6462 ➡ 6000
6943 ➡ 7000	3753 ➡ 4000	7819 ➡ 8000	2151 ➡ 2000
9857 ➡ 10000	5741 ➡ 6000	2015 ➡ 2000	6319 ➡ 6000
4211 ➡ 4000	9920 ➡ 10000	7213 ➡ 7000	3400 ➡ 3000
ANSWERS	**ANSWERS**	**ANSWERS**	**ANSWERS**
Maths Minute 5	**Maths Minute 5**	**Maths Minute 5**	**Maths Minute 5**

Andrew Brodie Publications
© A & C Black Publishers Ltd.

Andrew Brodie Publications
© A & C Black Publishers Ltd.

Andrew Brodie Publications
© A & C Black Publishers Ltd.

Andrew Brodie Publications
© A & C Black Publishers Ltd.

◆ Name	● Name	▲ Name	✶ Name
Number bonds to 20	**Number bonds to 20**	**Number bonds to 20**	**Number bonds to 20**
$3 + 5 =$	$4 + 3 =$	$7 + 4 =$	$3 + 4 =$
$6 + 2 =$	$9 + 4 =$	$3 + 3 =$	$8 + 8 =$
$7 + 4 =$	$2 + 7 =$	$2 + 9 =$	$6 + 8 =$
$5 + 8 =$	$3 + 11 =$	$5 + 6 =$	$5 + 7 =$
$13 + 3 =$	$14 + 6 =$	$4 + 13 =$	$9 + 11 =$
$14 + 6 =$	$8 + 5 =$	$5 + 12 =$	$11 + 8 =$
$12 + 4 =$	$7 + 7 =$	$2 + 18 =$	$3 + 16 =$
$13 + 5 =$	$11 + 6 =$	$13 + 4 =$	$2 + 18 =$
$8 + 8 =$	$12 + 3 =$	$14 + 4 =$	$15 + 4 =$
$10 + 9 =$	$15 + 5 =$	$16 + 3 =$	$16 + 3 =$
$8 + 12 =$	$6 + 8 =$	$15 + 5 =$	$7 + 9 =$
$12 + 8 =$	$8 + 6 =$	$5 + 15 =$	$9 + 7 =$
$20 - 8 =$	$14 - 8 =$	$20 - 5 =$	$16 - 9 =$
$20 - 12 =$	$14 - 6 =$	$20 - 15 =$	$16 - 7 =$
$14 - 3 =$	$8 - 6 =$	$20 - 6 =$	$12 - 6 =$
$16 - 8 =$	$13 - 7 =$	$20 - 8 =$	$14 - 7 =$
$9 - 4 =$	$11 - 6 =$	$20 - 11 =$	$18 - 9 =$
$8 - 5 =$	$9 - 4 =$	$20 - 15 =$	$20 - 10 =$
$19 - 10 =$	$17 - 3 =$	$20 - 17 =$	$14 - 6 =$
$19 - 9 =$	$14 - 13 =$	$20 - 3 =$	$19 - 9 =$
$19 - 8 =$	$12 - 8 =$	$18 - 10 =$	$14 - 4 =$
$17 - 10 =$	$10 - 4 =$	$14 - 10 =$	$17 - 7 =$
$16 - 10 =$	$16 - 10 =$	$15 - 9 =$	$16 - 6 =$
$11 - 10 =$	$16 - 9 =$	$15 - 8 =$	$13 - 3 =$
Maths Minute 6	**Maths Minute 6**	**Maths Minute 6**	**Maths Minute 6**

Andrew Brodie Publications
© A & C Black Publishers Ltd.   © A & C Black Publishers Ltd.   © A & C Black Publishers Ltd.   © A & C Black Publishers Ltd.

◆ ANSWERS
Number bonds to 20

● ANSWERS
Number bonds to 20

▲ ANSWERS
Number bonds to 20

✷ ANSWERS
Number bonds to 20

◆	●	▲	✷
$3 + 5 = 8$	$4 + 3 = 7$	$7 + 4 = 11$	$3 + 4 = 7$
$6 + 2 = 8$	$9 + 4 = 13$	$3 + 3 = 6$	$8 + 8 = 16$
$7 + 4 = 11$	$2 + 7 = 9$	$2 + 9 = 11$	$6 + 8 = 14$
$5 + 8 = 13$	$3 + 11 = 14$	$5 + 6 = 11$	$5 + 7 = 12$
$13 + 3 = 16$	$14 + 6 = 20$	$4 + 13 = 17$	$9 + 11 = 20$
$14 + 6 = 20$	$8 + 5 = 13$	$5 + 12 = 17$	$11 + 8 = 19$
$12 + 4 = 16$	$7 + 7 = 14$	$2 + 18 = 20$	$3 + 16 = 19$
$13 + 5 = 18$	$11 + 6 = 17$	$13 + 4 = 17$	$2 + 18 = 20$
$8 + 8 = 16$	$12 + 3 = 15$	$14 + 4 = 18$	$15 + 4 = 19$
$10 + 9 = 19$	$15 + 5 = 20$	$16 + 3 = 19$	$16 + 3 = 19$
$8 + 12 = 20$	$6 + 8 = 14$	$15 + 5 = 20$	$7 + 9 = 16$
$12 + 8 = 20$	$8 + 6 = 14$	$5 + 15 = 20$	$9 + 7 = 16$
$20 - 8 = 12$	$14 - 8 = 6$	$20 - 5 = 15$	$16 - 9 = 7$
$20 - 12 = 8$	$14 - 6 = 8$	$20 - 15 = 5$	$16 - 7 = 9$
$14 - 3 = 11$	$8 - 6 = 2$	$20 - 6 = 14$	$12 - 6 = 6$
$16 - 8 = 8$	$13 - 7 = 6$	$20 - 8 = 12$	$14 - 7 = 7$
$9 - 4 = 5$	$11 - 6 = 5$	$20 - 11 = 9$	$18 - 9 = 9$
$8 - 5 = 3$	$9 - 4 = 5$	$20 - 15 = 5$	$20 - 10 = 10$
$19 - 10 = 9$	$17 - 3 = 14$	$20 - 17 = 3$	$14 - 6 = 8$
$19 - 9 = 10$	$14 - 13 = 1$	$20 - 3 = 17$	$19 - 9 = 10$
$19 - 8 = 11$	$12 - 8 = 4$	$18 - 10 = 8$	$14 - 4 = 10$
$17 - 10 = 7$	$10 - 4 = 6$	$14 - 10 = 4$	$17 - 7 = 10$
$16 - 10 = 6$	$16 - 10 = 6$	$15 - 9 = 6$	$16 - 6 = 10$
$11 - 10 = 1$	$16 - 9 = 7$	$15 - 8 = 7$	$13 - 3 = 10$

ANSWERS
Maths Minute 6

Andrew Brodie Publications
© A & C Black Publishers Ltd.

ANSWERS
Maths Minute 6

Andrew Brodie Publications
© A & C Black Publishers Ltd.

ANSWERS
Maths Minute 6

Andrew Brodie Publications
© A & C Black Publishers Ltd.

ANSWERS
Maths Minute 6

Andrew Brodie Publications
© A & C Black Publishers Ltd.

◆ Name	● Name	▲ Name	✳ Name
Number bonds to 30	Number bonds to 30	Number bonds to 30	Number bonds to 30
$20 + 3 =$	$16 + 4 =$	$17 + 8 =$	$20 + 7 =$
$20 + 4 =$	$26 + 4 =$	$14 + 6 =$	$10 + 17 =$
$16 + 8 =$	$3 + 5 =$	$4 + 8 =$	$6 + 3 =$
$17 + 9 =$	$13 + 5 =$	$14 + 8 =$	$6 + 13 =$
$18 + 9 =$	$23 + 5 =$	$24 + 3 =$	$6 + 23 =$
$22 + 6 =$	$17 + 8 =$	$18 + 11 =$	$16 + 13 =$
$14 + 14 =$	$15 + 15 =$	$14 + 7 =$	$11 + 5 =$
$16 + 12 =$	$6 + 2 =$	$16 + 14 =$	$14 + 8 =$
$13 + 13 =$	$16 + 12 =$	$8 + 16 =$	$26 + 4 =$
$16 + 10 =$	$17 + 11 =$	$10 + 15 =$	$23 + 7 =$
$25 + 5 =$	$11 + 17 =$	$19 + 8 =$	$14 + 9 =$
$5 + 25 =$	$17 + 12 =$	$8 + 19 =$	$9 + 14 =$
$30 - 5 =$	$28 - 11 =$	$27 - 19 =$	$23 - 9 =$
$30 - 25 =$	$19 - 9 =$	$27 - 8 =$	$23 - 14 =$
$16 - 6 =$	$9 - 5 =$	$29 - 6 =$	$15 - 5 =$
$24 - 4 =$	$19 - 5 =$	$29 - 16 =$	$17 - 8 =$
$17 - 7 =$	$19 - 15 =$	$29 - 26 =$	$27 - 8 =$
$28 - 8 =$	$29 - 5 =$	$27 - 13 =$	$19 - 6 =$
$13 - 6 =$	$29 - 15 =$	$15 - 13 =$	$18 - 9 =$
$17 - 9 =$	$23 - 8 =$	$22 - 7 =$	$28 - 19 =$
$30 - 8 =$	$24 - 8 =$	$15 - 3 =$	$27 - 14 =$
$28 - 10 =$	$17 - 17 =$	$26 - 13 =$	$21 - 16 =$
$26 - 7 =$	$28 - 8 =$	$18 - 7 =$	$24 - 17 =$
$23 - 7 =$	$28 - 17 =$	$25 - 6 =$	$25 - 18 =$
Maths Minute 7	**Maths Minute 7**	**Maths Minute 7**	**Maths Minute 7**

Andrew Brodie Publications
© A & C Black Publishers Ltd.   Andrew Brodie Publications
© A & C Black Publishers Ltd.   Andrew Brodie Publications
© A & C Black Publishers Ltd.   Andrew Brodie Publications
© A & C Black Publishers Ltd.

◆	●	▲	✴
$20 + 3 = 23$	$16 + 4 = 20$	$17 + 8 = 25$	$20 + 7 = 27$
$20 + 4 = 24$	$26 + 4 = 30$	$14 + 6 = 20$	$10 + 17 = 27$
$16 + 8 = 24$	$3 + 5 = 8$	$4 + 8 = 12$	$6 + 3 = 9$
$17 + 9 = 26$	$13 + 5 = 18$	$14 + 8 = 22$	$6 + 13 = 19$
$18 + 9 = 27$	$23 + 5 = 28$	$24 + 3 = 27$	$6 + 23 = 29$
$22 + 6 = 28$	$17 + 8 = 25$	$18 + 11 = 29$	$16 + 13 = 29$
$14 + 14 = 28$	$15 + 15 = 30$	$14 + 7 = 21$	$11 + 5 = 16$
$16 + 12 = 28$	$6 + 2 = 8$	$16 + 14 = 30$	$14 + 8 = 22$
$13 + 13 = 26$	$16 + 12 = 28$	$8 + 16 = 24$	$26 + 4 = 30$
$16 + 10 = 26$	$17 + 11 = 28$	$10 + 15 = 25$	$23 + 7 = 30$
$25 + 5 = 30$	$11 + 17 = 28$	$19 + 8 = 27$	$14 + 9 = 23$
$5 + 25 = 30$	$17 + 12 = 29$	$8 + 19 = 27$	$9 + 14 = 23$
$30 - 5 = 25$	$28 - 11 = 17$	$27 - 19 = 8$	$23 - 9 = 14$
$30 - 25 = 5$	$19 - 9 = 10$	$27 - 8 = 19$	$23 - 14 = 9$
$16 - 6 = 10$	$9 - 5 = 4$	$29 - 6 = 23$	$15 - 5 = 10$
$24 - 4 = 20$	$19 - 5 = 14$	$29 - 16 = 13$	$17 - 8 = 9$
$17 - 7 = 10$	$19 - 15 = 4$	$29 - 26 = 3$	$27 - 8 = 19$
$28 - 8 = 20$	$29 - 5 = 24$	$27 - 13 = 14$	$19 - 6 = 13$
$13 - 6 = 7$	$29 - 15 = 14$	$15 - 13 = 2$	$18 - 9 = 9$
$17 - 9 = 8$	$23 - 8 = 15$	$22 - 7 = 15$	$28 - 19 = 9$
$30 - 8 = 22$	$24 - 8 = 16$	$15 - 3 = 12$	$27 - 14 = 13$
$28 - 10 = 18$	$17 - 17 = 0$	$26 - 13 = 13$	$21 - 16 = 5$
$26 - 7 = 19$	$28 - 8 = 20$	$18 - 7 = 11$	$24 - 17 = 7$
$23 - 7 = 16$	$28 - 17 = 11$	$25 - 6 = 19$	$25 - 18 = 7$

Andrew Brodie Publications
© A & C Black Publishers Ltd.

Andrew Brodie Publications
© A & C Black Publishers Ltd.

Andrew Brodie Publications
© A & C Black Publishers Ltd.

Andrew Brodie Publications
© A & C Black Publishers Ltd.

◆ Name	● Name	▲ Name	✳ Name
Doubling 2 digit numbers	**Doubling 2 digit numbers**	**Doubling 2 digit numbers**	**Doubling 2 digit numbers**
double 18 =	double 60 =	double 40 =	double 50 =
double 88 =	double 61 =	double 90 =	double 99 =
double 10 =	double 57 =	double 29 =	double 38 =
double 46 =	double 19 =	double 85 =	double 39 =
double 82 =	double 29 =	double 11 =	double 43 =
double 52 =	double 56 =	double 51 =	double 13 =
double 13 =	double 72 =	double 58 =	double 73 =
double 70 =	double 10 =	double 26 =	double 75 =
double 33 =	double 78 =	double 53 =	double 31 =
double 80 =	double 33 =	double 30 =	double 91 =
double 16 =	double 50 =	double 14 =	double 11 =
double 93 =	double 81 =	double 70 =	double 98 =
double 69 =	double 13 =	double 77 =	double 47 =
double 99 =	double 91 =	double 34 =	double 81 =
double 22 =	double 26 =	double 15 =	double 29 =
double 91 =	double 86 =	double 48 =	double 68 =
double 67 =	double 21 =	double 80 =	double 79 =
double 73 =	double 93 =	double 37 =	double 52 =
double 74 =	double 39 =	double 21 =	double 24 =
double 58 =	double 35 =	double 63 =	double 64 =
double 90 =	double 15 =	double 42 =	double 58 =
double 76 =	double 41 =	double 43 =	double 35 =
double 89 =	double 95 =	double 61 =	double 63 =
double 63 =	double 25 =	double 17 =	double 18 =
Maths Minute 8	**Maths Minute 8**	**Maths Minute 8**	**Maths Minute 8**

Andrew Brodie Publications
© A & C Black Publishers Ltd.
Andrew Brodie Publications
© A & C Black Publishers Ltd.
Andrew Brodie Publications
© A & C Black Publishers Ltd.
Andrew Brodie Publications
© A & C Black Publishers Ltd.

double 18 = 36

double 88 = 176

double 10 = 20

double 46 = 92

double 82 = 164

double 52 = 104

double 13 = 26

double 70 = 140

double 33 = 66

double 80 = 160

double 16 = 32

double 93 = 186

double 69 = 138

double 99 = 198

double 22 = 44

double 91 = 182

double 67 = 134

double 73 = 146

double 74 = 148

double 58 = 116

double 90 = 180

double 76 = 152

double 89 = 178

double 60 = 120

double 61 = 122

double 57 = 114

double 19 = 38

double 29 = 58

double 56 = 112

double 72 = 144

double 10 = 20

double 78 = 156

double 33 = 66

double 50 = 100

double 81 = 162

double 13 = 26

double 91 = 182

double 26 = 52

double 86 = 172

double 21 = 42

double 93 = 186

double 39 = 78

double 35 = 70

double 15 = 30

double 41 = 82

double 95 = 190

double 40 = 80

double 90 = 180

double 29 = 58

double 85 = 170

double 11 = 22

double 51 = 102

double 58 = 116

double 26 = 52

double 53 = 106

double 30 = 60

double 14 = 28

double 70 = 140

double 77 = 154

double 34 = 68

double 15 = 30

double 48 = 96

double 80 = 160

double 37 = 74

double 21 = 42

double 63 = 126

double 42 = 84

double 43 = 86

double 61 = 122

double 50 = 100

double 99 = 198

double 38 = 76

double 39 = 78

double 43 = 86

double 13 = 26

double 73 = 146

double 75 = 150

double 31 = 62

double 91 = 182

double 11 = 22

double 98 = 196

double 47 = 94

double 81 = 162

double 29 = 58

double 68 = 136

double 79 = 158

double 52 = 104

double 24 = 48

double 64 = 128

double 58 = 116

double 35 = 70

double 63 = 126

◆ Name	● Name	▲ Name	✳ Name
100 minus 2 digit numbers	100 minus 2 digit numbers	100 minus 2 digit numbers	100 minus 2 digit numbers
$100 - 21 =$	$100 - 14 =$	$100 - 11 =$	$100 - 12 =$
$100 - 15 =$	$100 - 46 =$	$100 - 30 =$	$100 - 41 =$
$100 - 36 =$	$100 - 10 =$	$100 - 56 =$	$100 - 70 =$
$100 - 92 =$	$100 - 28 =$	$100 - 59 =$	$100 - 28 =$
$100 - 31 =$	$100 - 56 =$	$100 - 91 =$	$100 - 78 =$
$100 - 83 =$	$100 - 66 =$	$100 - 19 =$	$100 - 97 =$
$100 - 29 =$	$100 - 25 =$	$100 - 95 =$	$100 - 90 =$
$100 - 91 =$	$100 - 40 =$	$100 - 24 =$	$100 - 69 =$
$100 - 45 =$	$100 - 92 =$	$100 - 39 =$	$100 - 24 =$
$100 - 88 =$	$100 - 12 =$	$100 - 79 =$	$100 - 39 =$
$100 - 12 =$	$100 - 64 =$	$100 - 10 =$	$100 - 68 =$
$100 - 50 =$	$100 - 31 =$	$100 - 80 =$	$100 - 13 =$
$100 - 81 =$	$100 - 84 =$	$100 - 36 =$	$100 - 48 =$
$100 - 53 =$	$100 - 19 =$	$100 - 64 =$	$100 - 63 =$
$100 - 97 =$	$100 - 72 =$	$100 - 15 =$	$100 - 50 =$
$100 - 16 =$	$100 - 49 =$	$100 - 16 =$	$100 - 21 =$
$100 - 73 =$	$100 - 50 =$	$100 - 50 =$	$100 - 86 =$
$100 - 58 =$	$100 - 34 =$	$100 - 33 =$	$100 - 33 =$
$100 - 20 =$	$100 - 61 =$	$100 - 72 =$	$100 - 56 =$
$100 - 60 =$	$100 - 21 =$	$100 - 49 =$	$100 - 16 =$
$100 - 38 =$	$100 - 77 =$	$100 - 87 =$	$100 - 81 =$
$100 - 64 =$	$100 - 59 =$	$100 - 27 =$	$100 - 36 =$
$100 - 69 =$	$100 - 24 =$	$100 - 70 =$	$100 - 55 =$
$100 - 40 =$	$100 - 38 =$	$100 - 44 =$	$100 - 19 =$

Maths Minute 9

Andrew Brodie Publications
© A & C Black Publishers Ltd.

◆ ANSWERS	● ANSWERS	▲ ANSWERS	✴ ANSWERS
100 minus 2 digit numbers	100 minus 2 digit numbers	100 minus 2 digit numbers	100 minus 2 digit numbers
100 – 21 = 79	100 – 14 = 86	100 – 11 = 89	100 – 12 = 88
100 – 15 = 85	100 – 46 = 54	100 – 30 = 70	100 – 41 = 59
100 – 36 = 64	100 – 10 = 90	100 – 56 = 44	100 – 70 = 30
100 – 92 = 8	100 – 28 = 72	100 – 59 = 41	100 – 28 = 72
100 – 31 = 69	100 – 56 = 44	100 – 91 = 9	100 – 78 = 22
100 – 83 = 17	100 – 66 = 34	100 – 19 = 81	100 – 97 = 3
100 – 29 = 71	100 – 25 = 75	100 – 95 = 5	100 – 90 = 10
100 – 91 = 9	100 – 40 = 60	100 – 24 = 76	100 – 69 = 31
100 – 45 = 55	100 – 92 = 8	100 – 39 = 61	100 – 24 = 76
100 – 88 = 12	100 – 12 = 88	100 – 79 = 21	100 – 39 = 61
100 – 12 = 88	100 – 64 = 36	100 – 10 = 90	100 – 68 = 32
100 – 50 = 50	100 – 31 = 69	100 – 80 = 20	100 – 13 = 87
100 – 81 = 19	100 – 84 = 16	100 – 36 = 64	100 – 48 = 52
100 – 53 = 47	100 – 19 = 81	100 – 64 = 36	100 – 63 = 37
100 – 97 = 3	100 – 72 = 28	100 – 15 = 85	100 – 50 = 50
100 – 16 = 84	100 – 49 = 51	100 – 16 = 84	100 – 21 = 79
100 – 73 = 27	100 – 50 = 50	100 – 50 = 50	100 – 86 = 14
100 – 58 = 42	100 – 34 = 66	100 – 33 = 67	100 – 33 = 67
100 – 20 = 80	100 – 61 = 39	100 – 72 = 28	100 – 56 = 44
100 – 60 = 40	100 – 21 = 79	100 – 49 = 51	100 – 16 = 84
100 – 38 = 62	100 – 77 = 23	100 – 87 = 13	100 – 81 = 19
100 – 64 = 36	100 – 59 = 41	100 – 27 = 73	100 – 36 = 64
100 – 69 = 31	100 – 24 = 76	100 – 70 = 30	100 – 55 = 45
100 – 40 = 60	100 – 38 = 62	100 – 44 = 56	100 – 19 = 81
ANSWERS	**ANSWERS**	**ANSWERS**	**ANSWERS**
Maths Minute 9	**Maths Minute 9**	**Maths Minute 9**	**Maths Minute 9**

Andrew Brodie Publications © A & C Black Publishers Ltd.

Andrew Brodie Publications © A & C Black Publishers Ltd.

Andrew Brodie Publications © A & C Black Publishers Ltd.

Andrew Brodie Publications © A & C Black Publishers Ltd.

◆ Name	● Name	▲ Name	✹ Name
10 minus numbers with 1 decimal place	10 minus numbers with 1 decimal place	10 minus numbers with 1 decimal place	10 minus numbers with 1 decimal place
10 − 1·6 =	10 − 1·3 =	10 − 1·5 =	10 − 1·7 =
10 − 3·6 =	10 − 6·2 =	10 − 8·4 =	10 − 8·6 =
10 − 3·7 =	10 − 9·8 =	10 − 1·7 =	10 − 9·1 =
10 − 3·8 =	10 − 9·9 =	10 − 8·3 =	10 − 1·5 =
10 − 7·4 =	10 − 3·1 =	10 − 3·6 =	10 − 8·8 =
10 − 1·7 =	10 − 5·4 =	10 − 3·7 =	10 − 3·1 =
10 − 2·5 =	10 − 8·6 =	10 − 5·9 =	10 − 5·7 =
10 − 9·9 =	10 − 2·6 =	10 − 4·1 =	10 − 7·8 =
10 − 5·2 =	10 − 2·7 =	10 − 7·8 =	10 − 2·7 =
10 − 9·6 =	10 − 2·8 =	10 − 5·4 =	10 − 5·8 =
10 − 6·8 =	10 − 5·6 =	10 − 6·2 =	10 − 6·1 =
10 − 8·4 =	10 − 8·3 =	10 − 3·8 =	10 − 1·9 =
10 − 4·1 =	10 − 7·9 =	10 − 7·1 =	10 − 3·4 =
10 − 6·7 =	10 − 1·7 =	10 − 4·3 =	10 − 5·5 =
10 − 4·9 =	10 − 6·6 =	10 − 6·9 =	10 − 7·7 =
10 − 5·9 =	10 − 5·1 =	10 − 2·5 =	10 − 6·6 =
10 − 2·4 =	10 − 7·1 =	10 − 6·7 =	10 − 3·6 =
10 − 7·6 =	10 − 3·3 =	10 − 1·9 =	10 − 2·6 =
10 − 6·3 =	10 − 4·9 =	10 − 5·5 =	10 − 6·8 =
10 − 1·8 =	10 − 6·7 =	10 − 9·3 =	10 − 4·1 =
10 − 4·3 =	10 − 4·6 =	10 − 4·2 =	10 − 4·2 =
10 − 8·9 =	10 − 1·9 =	10 − 2·1 =	10 − 4·3 =
10 − 2·3 =	10 − 4·8 =	10 − 9·6 =	10 − 9·3 =
10 − 5·4 =	10 − 3·9 =	10 − 2·9 =	10 − 2·0 =

Maths Minute 10

Andrew Brodie Publications
© A & C Black Publishers Ltd.

Maths Minute 10

Andrew Brodie Publications
© A & C Black Publishers Ltd.

Maths Minute 10

Andrew Brodie Publications
© A & C Black Publishers Ltd.

Maths Minute 10

Andrew Brodie Publications
© A & C Black Publishers Ltd.

◆	●	▲	✸
$10 - 1{\cdot}6 = 8{\cdot}4$	$10 - 1{\cdot}3 = 8{\cdot}7$	$10 - 1{\cdot}5 = 8{\cdot}5$	$10 - 1{\cdot}7 = 8{\cdot}3$
$10 - 3{\cdot}6 = 6{\cdot}4$	$10 - 6{\cdot}2 = 3{\cdot}8$	$10 - 8{\cdot}4 = 1{\cdot}6$	$10 - 8{\cdot}6 = 1{\cdot}4$
$10 - 3{\cdot}7 = 6{\cdot}3$	$10 - 9{\cdot}8 = 0{\cdot}2$	$10 - 1{\cdot}7 = 8{\cdot}3$	$10 - 9{\cdot}1 = 0{\cdot}9$
$10 - 3{\cdot}8 = 6{\cdot}2$	$10 - 9{\cdot}9 = 0{\cdot}1$	$10 - 8{\cdot}3 = 1{\cdot}7$	$10 - 1{\cdot}5 = 8{\cdot}5$
$10 - 7{\cdot}4 = 2{\cdot}6$	$10 - 3{\cdot}1 = 6{\cdot}9$	$10 - 3{\cdot}6 = 6{\cdot}4$	$10 - 8{\cdot}8 = 1{\cdot}2$
$10 - 1{\cdot}7 = 8{\cdot}3$	$10 - 5{\cdot}4 = 4{\cdot}6$	$10 - 3{\cdot}7 = 6{\cdot}3$	$10 - 3{\cdot}1 = 6{\cdot}9$
$10 - 2{\cdot}5 = 7{\cdot}5$	$10 - 8{\cdot}6 = 1{\cdot}4$	$10 - 5{\cdot}9 = 4{\cdot}1$	$10 - 5{\cdot}7 = 4{\cdot}3$
$10 - 9{\cdot}9 = 0{\cdot}1$	$10 - 2{\cdot}6 = 7{\cdot}4$	$10 - 4{\cdot}1 = 5{\cdot}9$	$10 - 7{\cdot}8 = 2{\cdot}2$
$10 - 5{\cdot}2 = 4{\cdot}8$	$10 - 2{\cdot}7 = 7{\cdot}3$	$10 - 7{\cdot}8 = 2{\cdot}2$	$10 - 2{\cdot}7 = 7{\cdot}3$
$10 - 9{\cdot}6 = 0{\cdot}4$	$10 - 2{\cdot}8 = 7{\cdot}2$	$10 - 5{\cdot}4 = 4{\cdot}6$	$10 - 5{\cdot}8 = 4{\cdot}2$
$10 - 6{\cdot}8 = 3{\cdot}2$	$10 - 5{\cdot}6 = 4{\cdot}4$	$10 - 6{\cdot}2 = 3{\cdot}8$	$10 - 6{\cdot}1 = 3{\cdot}9$
$10 - 8{\cdot}4 = 1{\cdot}6$	$10 - 8{\cdot}3 = 1{\cdot}7$	$10 - 3{\cdot}8 = 6{\cdot}2$	$10 - 1{\cdot}9 = 8{\cdot}1$
$10 - 4{\cdot}1 = 5{\cdot}9$	$10 - 7{\cdot}9 = 2{\cdot}1$	$10 - 7{\cdot}1 = 2{\cdot}9$	$10 - 3{\cdot}4 = 6{\cdot}6$
$10 - 6{\cdot}7 = 3{\cdot}3$	$10 - 1{\cdot}7 = 8{\cdot}3$	$10 - 4{\cdot}3 = 5{\cdot}7$	$10 - 5{\cdot}5 = 4{\cdot}5$
$10 - 4{\cdot}9 = 5{\cdot}1$	$10 - 6{\cdot}6 = 3{\cdot}4$	$10 - 6{\cdot}9 = 3{\cdot}1$	$10 - 7{\cdot}7 = 2{\cdot}3$
$10 - 5{\cdot}9 = 4{\cdot}1$	$10 - 5{\cdot}1 = 4{\cdot}9$	$10 - 2{\cdot}5 = 7{\cdot}5$	$10 - 6{\cdot}6 = 3{\cdot}4$
$10 - 2{\cdot}4 = 7{\cdot}6$	$10 - 7{\cdot}1 = 2{\cdot}9$	$10 - 6{\cdot}7 = 3{\cdot}3$	$10 - 3{\cdot}6 = 6{\cdot}4$
$10 - 7{\cdot}6 = 2{\cdot}4$	$10 - 3{\cdot}3 = 6{\cdot}7$	$10 - 1{\cdot}9 = 8{\cdot}1$	$10 - 2{\cdot}6 = 7{\cdot}4$
$10 - 6{\cdot}3 = 3{\cdot}7$	$10 - 4{\cdot}9 = 5{\cdot}1$	$10 - 5{\cdot}5 = 4{\cdot}5$	$10 - 6{\cdot}8 = 3{\cdot}2$
$10 - 1{\cdot}8 = 8{\cdot}2$	$10 - 6{\cdot}7 = 3{\cdot}3$	$10 - 9{\cdot}3 = 0{\cdot}7$	$10 - 4{\cdot}1 = 5{\cdot}9$
$10 - 4{\cdot}3 = 5{\cdot}7$	$10 - 4{\cdot}6 = 5{\cdot}4$	$10 - 4{\cdot}2 = 5{\cdot}8$	$10 - 4{\cdot}2 = 5{\cdot}8$
$10 - 8{\cdot}9 = 1{\cdot}1$	$10 - 1{\cdot}9 = 8{\cdot}1$	$10 - 2{\cdot}1 = 7{\cdot}9$	$10 - 4{\cdot}3 = 5{\cdot}7$
$10 - 2{\cdot}3 = 7{\cdot}7$	$10 - 4{\cdot}8 = 5{\cdot}2$	$10 - 9{\cdot}6 = 0{\cdot}4$	$10 - 9{\cdot}3 = 0{\cdot}7$
$10 - 5{\cdot}4 = 4{\cdot}6$	$10 - 3{\cdot}9 = 6{\cdot}1$	$10 - 2{\cdot}9 = 7{\cdot}1$	$10 - 2{\cdot}0 = 8$

Andrew Brodie Publications © A & C Black Publishers Ltd.	Andrew Brodie Publications © A & C Black Publishers Ltd.	Andrew Brodie Publications © A & C Black Publishers Ltd.	Andrew Brodie Publications © A & C Black Publishers Ltd.

◆ Name

Fill the gaps in the addition sums

3·6 + ☐ = 4

8·2 + ☐ = 9

3·4 + ☐ = 4

8·3 + ☐ = 9

2·9 + ☐ = 3

5·4 + ☐ = 6

1·1 + ☐ = 2

5·2 + ☐ = 6

9·4 + ☐ = 10

3·8 + ☐ = 4

6·9 + ☐ = 7

1·3 + ☐ = 2

7·6 + ☐ = 8

2·6 + ☐ = 3

7·8 + ☐ = 8

4·1 + ☐ = 5

9·9 + ☐ = 10

2·3 + ☐ = 3

6·3 + ☐ = 7

4·4 + ☐ = 5

4·5 + ☐ = 5

6·1 + ☐ = 7

5·6 + ☐ = 6

1·5 + ☐ = 2

Maths Minute 11

Andrew Brodie Publications
© A & C Black Publishers Ltd.

● Name

Fill the gaps in the addition sums

3·2 + ☐ = 4

9·1 + ☐ = 10

6·7 + ☐ = 7

1·2 + ☐ = 2

5·8 + ☐ = 6

2·5 + ☐ = 3

9·6 + ☐ = 10

3·4 + ☐ = 4

6·8 + ☐ = 7

1·3 + ☐ = 2

8·4 + ☐ = 9

4·1 + ☐ = 5

5·4 + ☐ = 6

1·4 + ☐ = 2

6·9 + ☐ = 7

3·9 + ☐ = 4

7·9 + ☐ = 8

2·1 + ☐ = 3

5·2 + ☐ = 6

8·2 + ☐ = 9

4·3 + ☐ = 5

7·7 + ☐ = 8

4·7 + ☐ = 5

2·2 + ☐ = 3

Maths Minute 11

Andrew Brodie Publications
© A & C Black Publishers Ltd.

▲ Name

Fill the gaps in the addition sums

1·3 + ☐ = 2

3·2 + ☐ = 4

3·4 + ☐ = 4

4·1 + ☐ = 5

6·2 + ☐ = 7

1·4 + ☐ = 2

9·6 + ☐ = 10

6·4 + ☐ = 7

5·1 + ☐ = 6

8·8 + ☐ = 9

1·9 + ☐ = 2

8·4 + ☐ = 9

4·2 + ☐ = 5

5·8 + ☐ = 6

3·8 + ☐ = 4

6·6 + ☐ = 7

2·5 + ☐ = 3

7·7 + ☐ = 8

5·5 + ☐ = 6

2·6 + ☐ = 3

7·8 + ☐ = 8

4·9 + ☐ = 5

9·3 + ☐ = 10

2·8 + ☐ = 3

Maths Minute 11

Andrew Brodie Publications
© A & C Black Publishers Ltd.

✸ Name

Fill the gaps in the addition sums

2·6 + ☐ = 3

6·2 + ☐ = 7

4·2 + ☐ = 5

4·3 + ☐ = 5

1·1 + ☐ = 2

5·1 + ☐ = 6

8·6 + ☐ = 9

2·8 + ☐ = 3

9·9 + ☐ = 10

3·8 + ☐ = 4

6·6 + ☐ = 7

1·4 + ☐ = 2

5·7 + ☐ = 6

8·1 + ☐ = 9

4·4 + ☐ = 5

7·9 + ☐ = 8

1·8 + ☐ = 2

6·9 + ☐ = 7

5·9 + ☐ = 6

2·9 + ☐ = 3

3·6 + ☐ = 4

7·3 + ☐ = 8

7·8 + ☐ = 8

3·1 + ☐ = 4

Maths Minute 11

Andrew Brodie Publications
© A & C Black Publishers Ltd.

◆ ANSWERS

Fill the gaps in the addition sums

$3·6 + \boxed{0·4} = 4$

$8·2 + \boxed{0·8} = 9$

$3·4 + \boxed{0·6} = 4$

$8·3 + \boxed{0·7} = 9$

$2·9 + \boxed{0·1} = 3$

$5·4 + \boxed{0·6} = 6$

$1·1 + \boxed{0·9} = 2$

$5·2 + \boxed{0·8} = 6$

$9·4 + \boxed{0·6} = 10$

$3·8 + \boxed{0·2} = 4$

$6·9 + \boxed{0·1} = 7$

$1·3 + \boxed{0·7} = 2$

$7·6 + \boxed{0·4} = 8$

$2·6 + \boxed{0·4} = 3$

$7·8 + \boxed{0·2} = 8$

$4·1 + \boxed{0·9} = 5$

$9·9 + \boxed{0·1} = 10$

$2·3 + \boxed{0·7} = 3$

$6·3 + \boxed{0·7} = 7$

$4·4 + \boxed{0·6} = 5$

$4·5 + \boxed{0·5} = 5$

$6·1 + \boxed{0·9} = 7$

$5·6 + \boxed{0·4} = 6$

$1·5 + \boxed{0·5} = 2$

ANSWERS

Maths Minute 11

Andrew Brodie Publications
© A & C Black Publishers Ltd.

● ANSWERS

Fill the gaps in the addition sums

$3·2 + \boxed{0·8} = 4$

$9·1 + \boxed{0·9} = 10$

$6·7 + \boxed{0·3} = 7$

$1·2 + \boxed{0·8} = 2$

$5·8 + \boxed{0·2} = 6$

$2·5 + \boxed{0·5} = 3$

$9·6 + \boxed{0·4} = 10$

$3·4 + \boxed{0·6} = 4$

$6·8 + \boxed{0·2} = 7$

$1·3 + \boxed{0·7} = 2$

$8·4 + \boxed{0·6} = 9$

$4·1 + \boxed{0·9} = 5$

$5·4 + \boxed{0·6} = 6$

$1·4 + \boxed{0·6} = 2$

$6·9 + \boxed{0·1} = 7$

$3·9 + \boxed{0·1} = 4$

$7·9 + \boxed{0·1} = 8$

$2·1 + \boxed{0·9} = 3$

$5·2 + \boxed{0·8} = 6$

$8·2 + \boxed{0·8} = 9$

$4·3 + \boxed{0·7} = 5$

$7·7 + \boxed{0·3} = 8$

$4·7 + \boxed{0·3} = 5$

$2·2 + \boxed{0·8} = 3$

ANSWERS

Maths Minute 11

Andrew Brodie Publications
© A & C Black Publishers Ltd.

▲ ANSWERS

Fill the gaps in the addition sums

$1·3 + \boxed{0·7} = 2$

$3·2 + \boxed{0·8} = 4$

$3·4 + \boxed{0·6} = 4$

$4·1 + \boxed{0·9} = 5$

$6·2 + \boxed{0·8} = 7$

$1·4 + \boxed{0·6} = 2$

$9·6 + \boxed{0·4} = 10$

$6·4 + \boxed{0·6} = 7$

$5·1 + \boxed{0·9} = 6$

$8·8 + \boxed{0·2} = 9$

$1·9 + \boxed{0·1} = 2$

$8·4 + \boxed{0·6} = 9$

$4·2 + \boxed{0·8} = 5$

$5·8 + \boxed{0·2} = 6$

$3·8 + \boxed{0·2} = 4$

$6·6 + \boxed{0·4} = 7$

$2·5 + \boxed{0·5} = 3$

$7·7 + \boxed{0·3} = 8$

$5·5 + \boxed{0·5} = 6$

$2·6 + \boxed{0·4} = 3$

$7·8 + \boxed{0·2} = 8$

$4·9 + \boxed{0·1} = 5$

$9·3 + \boxed{0·7} = 10$

$2·8 + \boxed{0·2} = 3$

ANSWERS

Maths Minute 11

Andrew Brodie Publications
© A & C Black Publishers Ltd.

✶ ANSWERS

Fill the gaps in the addition sums

$2·6 + \boxed{0·4} = 3$

$6·2 + \boxed{0·8} = 7$

$4·2 + \boxed{0·8} = 5$

$4·3 + \boxed{0·7} = 5$

$1·1 + \boxed{0·9} = 2$

$5·1 + \boxed{0·9} = 6$

$8·6 + \boxed{0·4} = 9$

$2·8 + \boxed{0·2} = 3$

$9·9 + \boxed{0·1} = 10$

$3·8 + \boxed{0·2} = 4$

$6·6 + \boxed{0·4} = 7$

$1·4 + \boxed{0·6} = 2$

$5·7 + \boxed{0·3} = 6$

$8·1 + \boxed{0·9} = 9$

$4·4 + \boxed{0·6} = 5$

$7·9 + \boxed{0·1} = 8$

$1·8 + \boxed{0·2} = 2$

$6·9 + \boxed{0·1} = 7$

$5·9 + \boxed{0·1} = 6$

$2·9 + \boxed{0·1} = 3$

$3·6 + \boxed{0·4} = 4$

$7·3 + \boxed{0·7} = 8$

$7·8 + \boxed{0·2} = 8$

$3·1 + \boxed{0·9} = 4$

ANSWERS

Maths Minute 11

Andrew Brodie Publications
© A & C Black Publishers Ltd.

◆ Name	● Name	▲ Name	✳ Name
2, 3, 4 and 5 X tables	2, 3, 4 and 5 X tables	2, 3, 4 and 5 X tables	2, 3, 4 and 5 X tables
2 x 3 =	2 x 2 =	2 x 2 =	7 x 2 =
3 x 2 =	3 x 4 =	8 x 4 =	4 x 3 =
1 x 5 =	1 x 3 =	2 x 3 =	3 x 5 =
8 x 4 =	2 x 5 =	6 x 5 =	4 x 4 =
3 x 3 =	8 x 5 =	3 x 4 =	5 x 5 =
7 x 5 =	0 x 2 =	8 x 2 =	1 x 2 =
3 x 4 =	10 x 5 =	1 x 3 =	7 x 3 =
7 x 2 =	8 x 3 =	4 x 5 =	7 x 4 =
3 x 5 =	2 x 3 =	9 x 2 =	10 x 3 =
4 x 2 =	1 x 4 =	2 x 5 =	8 x 2 =
9 x 3 =	10 x 2 =	8 x 3 =	6 x 4 =
10 x 4 =	6 x 5 =	0 x 4 =	3 x 3 =
9 x 2 =	4 x 3 =	7 x 2 =	1 x 5 =
4 x 4 =	9 x 4 =	5 x 4 =	3 x 2 =
9 x 5 =	9 x 2 =	9 x 3 =	7 x 5 =
8 x 3 =	7 x 2 =	4 x 2 =	2 x 4 =
5 x 5 =	2 x 4 =	10 x 5 =	9 x 2 =
7 x 4 =	10 x 3 =	4 x 3 =	10 x 4 =
5 x 2 =	10 x 4 =	8 x 5 =	2 x 3 =
6 x 4 =	4 x 5 =	7 x 4 =	5 x 2 =
5 x 3 =	6 x 2 =	6 x 3 =	8 x 4 =
7 x 3 =	5 x 4 =	6 x 2 =	9 x 5 =
8 x 2 =	6 x 3 =	9 x 5 =	8 x 5 =
8 x 5 =	7 x 5 =	9 x 4 =	5 x 3 =
Maths Minute 12	**Maths Minute 12**	**Maths Minute 12**	**Maths Minute 12**

Andrew Brodie Publications © A & C Black Publishers Ltd.
Andrew Brodie Publications © A & C Black Publishers Ltd.
Andrew Brodie Publications © A & C Black Publishers Ltd.
Andrew Brodie Publications © A & C Black Publishers Ltd.

◆	●	▲	✶
2 x 3 = 6	2 x 2 = 4	2 x 2 = 4	7 x 2 = 14
3 x 2 = 6	3 x 4 = 12	8 x 4 = 32	4 x 3 = 12
1 x 5 = 5	1 x 3 = 3	2 x 3 = 6	3 x 5 = 15
8 x 4 = 32	2 x 5 = 10	6 x 5 = 30	4 x 4 = 16
3 x 3 = 9	8 x 5 = 40	3 x 4 = 12	5 x 5 = 25
7 x 5 = 35	0 x 2 = 0	8 x 2 = 16	1 x 2 = 2
3 x 4 = 12	10 x 5 = 50	1 x 3 = 3	7 x 3 = 21
7 x 2 = 14	8 x 3 = 24	4 x 5 = 20	7 x 4 = 28
3 x 5 = 15	2 x 3 = 6	9 x 2 = 18	10 x 3 = 30
4 x 2 = 8	1 x 4 = 4	2 x 5 = 10	8 x 2 = 16
9 x 3 = 27	10 x 2 = 20	8 x 3 = 24	6 x 4 = 24
10 x 4 = 40	6 x 5 = 30	0 x 4 = 4	3 x 3 = 9
9 x 2 = 18	4 x 3 = 12	7 x 2 = 14	1 x 5 = 5
4 x 4 = 16	9 x 4 = 36	5 x 4 = 20	3 x 2 = 6
9 x 5 = 45	9 x 2 = 18	9 x 3 = 27	7 x 5 = 35
8 x 3 = 24	7 x 2 = 14	4 x 2 = 8	2 x 4 = 8
5 x 5 = 25	2 x 4 = 8	10 x 5 = 50	9 x 2 = 18
7 x 4 = 28	10 x 3 = 30	4 x 3 = 12	10 x 4 = 40
5 x 2 = 10	10 x 4 = 40	8 x 5 = 40	2 x 3 = 6
6 x 4 = 24	4 x 5 = 20	7 x 4 = 28	5 x 2 = 10
5 x 3 = 15	6 x 2 = 12	6 x 3 = 18	8 x 4 = 32
7 x 3 = 21	5 x 4 = 20	6 x 2 = 12	9 x 5 = 45
8 x 2 = 16	6 x 3 = 18	9 x 5 = 45	8 x 5 = 40
8 x 5 = 40	7 x 5 = 35	9 x 4 = 36	5 x 3 = 15

Andrew Brodie Publications
© A & C Black Publishers Ltd.

Andrew Brodie Publications
© A & C Black Publishers Ltd.

Andrew Brodie Publications
© A & C Black Publishers Ltd.

Andrew Brodie Publications
© A & C Black Publishers Ltd.

◆ Name	● Name	▲ Name	✳ Name
6,7,8, and 9 X tables	6,7,8, and 9 X tables	6,7,8, and 9 X tables	6,7,8, and 9 X tables
2 x 6 =	1 x 6 =	7 x 6 =	10 x 6 =
1 x 7 =	2 x 7 =	6 x 8 =	6 x 6 =
10 x 8 =	1 x 8 =	1 x 6 =	8 x 7 =
0 x 9 =	9 x 9 =	1 x 7 =	5 x 8 =
9 x 7 =	10 x 7 =	2 x 9 =	1 x 9 =
9 x 9 =	3 x 6 =	9 x 6 =	3 x 7 =
10 x 9 =	5 x 8 =	9 x 9 =	5 x 9 =
10 x 6 =	10 x 8 =	7 x 8 =	10 x 6 =
4 x 8 =	5 x 6 =	4 x 9 =	6 x 9 =
5 x 7 =	8 x 7 =	2 x 7 =	8 x 7 =
9 x 8 =	7 x 9 =	5 x 8 =	6 x 8 =
6 x 6 =	8 x 6 =	3 x 8 =	9 x 7 =
6 x 9 =	10 x 9 =	8 x 6 =	5 x 6 =
3 x 7 =	6 x 7 =	10 x 9 =	8 x 8 =
5 x 9 =	2 x 8 =	6 x 7 =	4 x 9 =
3 x 8 =	7 x 6 =	0 x 8 =	7 x 7 =
7 x 8 =	6 x 8 =	2 x 6 =	7 x 9 =
8 x 6 =	4 x 7 =	8 x 9 =	9 x 6 =
2 x 9 =	9 x 6 =	5 x 7 =	4 x 8 =
7 x 7 =	8 x 9 =	3 x 9 =	2 x 8 =
8 x 8 =	3 x 9 =	9 x 8 =	9 x 9 =
4 x 6 =	4 x 9 =	9 x 7 =	4 x 6 =
4 x 7 =	9 x 8 =	10 x 7 =	10 x 8 =
9 x 6 =	7 x 7 =	3 x 6 =	4 x 7 =

Maths Minute 13

Andrew Brodie Publications
© A & C Black Publishers Ltd.

Maths Minute 13
Andrew Brodie Publications
© A & C Black Publishers Ltd.

Maths Minute 13
Andrew Brodie Publications
© A & C Black Publishers Ltd.

Maths Minute 13
Andrew Brodie Publications
© A & C Black Publishers Ltd.

◆ ANSWERS	● ANSWERS	▲ ANSWERS	✴ ANSWERS
6,7,8, and 9 X tables	6,7,8, and 9 X tables	6,7,8, and 9 X tables	6,7,8, and 9 X tables
2 x 6 = 12	1 x 6 = 6	7 x 6 = 42	10 x 6 = 60
1 x 7 = 7	2 x 7 = 14	6 x 8 = 48	6 x 6 = 36
10 x 8 = 80	1 x 8 = 8	1 x 6 = 6	8 x 7 = 56
0 x 9 = 0	9 x 9 = 81	1 x 7 = 7	5 x 8 = 40
9 x 7 = 63	10 x 7 = 70	2 x 9 = 18	1 x 9 = 9
9 x 9 = 81	3 x 6 = 18	9 x 6 = 54	3 x 7 = 21
10 x 9 = 90	5 x 8 = 40	9 x 9 = 81	5 x 9 = 45
10 x 6 = 60	10 x 8 = 80	7 x 8 = 56	10 x 6 = 60
4 x 8 = 32	5 x 6 = 30	4 x 9 = 36	6 x 9 = 54
5 x 7 = 35	8 x 7 = 56	2 x 7 = 14	8 x 7 = 56
9 x 8 = 72	7 x 9 = 63	5 x 8 = 40	6 x 8 = 48
6 x 6 = 36	8 x 6 = 48	3 x 8 = 24	9 x 7 = 63
6 x 9 = 54	10 x 9 = 90	8 x 6 = 48	5 x 6 = 30
3 x 7 = 21	6 x 7 = 42	10 x 9 = 90	8 x 8 = 64
5 x 9 = 45	2 x 8 = 16	6 x 7 = 42	4 x 9 = 36
3 x 8 = 24	7 x 6 = 42	0 x 8 = 0	7 x 7 = 49
7 x 8 = 56	6 x 8 = 48	2 x 6 = 12	7 x 9 = 63
8 x 6 = 48	4 x 7 = 28	8 x 9 = 72	9 x 6 = 54
2 x 9 = 18	9 x 6 = 54	5 x 7 = 35	4 x 8 = 32
7 x 7 = 49	8 x 9 = 72	3 x 9 = 27	2 x 8 = 16
8 x 8 = 64	3 x 9 = 27	9 x 8 = 72	9 x 9 = 81
4 x 6 = 24	4 x 9 = 36	9 x 7 = 63	4 x 6 = 24
4 x 7 = 28	9 x 8 = 72	10 x 7 = 70	10 x 8 = 80
9 x 6 = 54	7 x 7 = 49	3 x 6 = 18	4 x 7 = 28

ANSWERS	**ANSWERS**	**ANSWERS**	**ANSWERS**
Maths Minute 13	**Maths Minute 13**	**Maths Minute 13**	**Maths Minute 13**

Andrew Brodie Publications
© A & C Black Publishers Ltd.   Andrew Brodie Publications
© A & C Black Publishers Ltd.   Andrew Brodie Publications
© A & C Black Publishers Ltd.   Andrew Brodie Publications
© A & C Black Publishers Ltd.

◆ Name	● Name	▲ Name	✷ Name
Division within 2,3,4 and 5 x tables	Division within 2,3,4 and 5 x tables	Division within 2,3,4 and 5 x tables	Division within 2,3,4 and 5 x tables
$30 \div 3 =$	$6 \div 3 =$	$18 \div 2 =$	$9 \div 3 =$
$28 \div 4 =$	$6 \div 2 =$	$27 \div 3 =$	$21 \div 3 =$
$45 \div 5 =$	$18 \div 2 =$	$32 \div 4 =$	$20 \div 4 =$
$10 \div 2 =$	$36 \div 4 =$	$21 \div 3 =$	$4 \div 2 =$
$15 \div 3 =$	$40 \div 4 =$	$24 \div 4 =$	$16 \div 4 =$
$20 \div 5 =$	$15 \div 5 =$	$2 \div 2 =$	$30 \div 5 =$
$35 \div 5 =$	$40 \div 5 =$	$25 \div 5 =$	$24 \div 3 =$
$27 \div 3 =$	$30 \div 3 =$	$15 \div 3 =$	$25 \div 5 =$
$16 \div 4 =$	$28 \div 4 =$	$20 \div 5 =$	$20 \div 2 =$
$15 \div 5 =$	$16 \div 2 =$	$6 \div 2 =$	$45 \div 5 =$
$40 \div 4 =$	$20 \div 4 =$	$20 \div 4 =$	$28 \div 4 =$
$2 \div 2 =$	$24 \div 3 =$	$35 \div 5 =$	$8 \div 2 =$
$5 \div 5 =$	$5 \div 5 =$	$9 \div 3 =$	$50 \div 5 =$
$9 \div 3 =$	$10 \div 2 =$	$36 \div 4 =$	$32 \div 4 =$
$10 \div 5 =$	$30 \div 5 =$	$8 \div 2 =$	$18 \div 2 =$
$8 \div 2 =$	$21 \div 3 =$	$12 \div 4 =$	$16 \div 2 =$
$24 \div 3 =$	$45 \div 5 =$	$40 \div 5 =$	$4 \div 4 =$
$16 \div 2 =$	$14 \div 2 =$	$6 \div 3 =$	$6 \div 3 =$
$36 \div 4 =$	$50 \div 5 =$	$45 \div 5 =$	$20 \div 5 =$
$18 \div 3 =$	$12 \div 3 =$	$8 \div 4 =$	$18 \div 3 =$
$4 \div 2 =$	$16 \div 4 =$	$30 \div 3 =$	$10 \div 5 =$
$12 \div 4 =$	$8 \div 2 =$	$14 \div 2 =$	$15 \div 5 =$
$8 \div 4 =$	$9 \div 3 =$	$10 \div 5 =$	$12 \div 4 =$
$20 \div 2 =$	$4 \div 4 =$	$16 \div 2 =$	$12 \div 2 =$

Maths Minute 14

Andrew Brodie Publications
© A & C Black Publishers Ltd.

Maths Minute 14
Andrew Brodie Publications
© A & C Black Publishers Ltd.

Maths Minute 14
Andrew Brodie Publications
© A & C Black Publishers Ltd.

Maths Minute 14
Andrew Brodie Publications
© A & C Black Publishers Ltd.

$$30 \div 3 = 10$$
$$28 \div 4 = 7$$
$$45 \div 5 = 9$$
$$10 \div 2 = 5$$
$$15 \div 3 = 5$$
$$20 \div 5 = 4$$
$$35 \div 5 = 7$$
$$27 \div 3 = 9$$
$$16 \div 4 = 4$$
$$15 \div 5 = 3$$
$$40 \div 4 = 10$$
$$2 \div 2 = 1$$
$$5 \div 5 = 1$$
$$9 \div 3 = 3$$
$$10 \div 5 = 2$$
$$8 \div 2 = 4$$
$$24 \div 3 = 8$$
$$16 \div 2 = 8$$
$$36 \div 4 = 9$$
$$18 \div 3 = 6$$
$$4 \div 2 = 2$$
$$12 \div 4 = 3$$
$$8 \div 4 = 2$$
$$20 \div 2 = 10$$

ANSWERS
Maths Minute 14

Andrew Brodie Publications
© A & C Black Publishers Ltd.

$$6 \div 3 = 2$$
$$6 \div 2 = 3$$
$$18 \div 2 = 9$$
$$36 \div 4 = 9$$
$$40 \div 4 = 10$$
$$15 \div 5 = 3$$
$$40 \div 5 = 8$$
$$30 \div 3 = 10$$
$$28 \div 4 = 7$$
$$16 \div 2 = 8$$
$$20 \div 4 = 5$$
$$24 \div 3 = 8$$
$$5 \div 5 = 1$$
$$10 \div 2 = 5$$
$$30 \div 5 = 6$$
$$21 \div 3 = 7$$
$$45 \div 5 = 9$$
$$14 \div 2 = 7$$
$$50 \div 5 = 10$$
$$12 \div 3 = 4$$
$$16 \div 4 = 4$$
$$8 \div 2 = 4$$
$$9 \div 3 = 3$$
$$4 \div 4 = 1$$

ANSWERS
Maths Minute 14

Andrew Brodie Publications
© A & C Black Publishers Ltd.

$$18 \div 2 = 9$$
$$27 \div 3 = 9$$
$$32 \div 4 = 8$$
$$21 \div 3 = 7$$
$$24 \div 4 = 6$$
$$2 \div 2 = 1$$
$$25 \div 5 = 5$$
$$15 \div 3 = 5$$
$$20 \div 5 = 4$$
$$6 \div 2 = 3$$
$$20 \div 4 = 5$$
$$35 \div 5 = 7$$
$$9 \div 3 = 3$$
$$36 \div 4 = 9$$
$$8 \div 2 = 4$$
$$12 \div 4 = 3$$
$$40 \div 5 = 8$$
$$6 \div 3 = 2$$
$$45 \div 5 = 9$$
$$8 \div 4 = 2$$
$$30 \div 3 = 10$$
$$14 \div 2 = 7$$
$$10 \div 5 = 2$$
$$16 \div 2 = 8$$

ANSWERS
Maths Minute 14

Andrew Brodie Publications
© A & C Black Publishers Ltd.

$$9 \div 3 = 3$$
$$21 \div 3 = 7$$
$$20 \div 4 = 5$$
$$4 \div 2 = 2$$
$$16 \div 4 = 4$$
$$30 \div 5 = 6$$
$$24 \div 3 = 8$$
$$25 \div 5 = 5$$
$$20 \div 2 = 10$$
$$45 \div 5 = 9$$
$$28 \div 4 = 7$$
$$8 \div 2 = 4$$
$$50 \div 5 = 10$$
$$32 \div 4 = 8$$
$$18 \div 2 = 9$$
$$16 \div 2 = 8$$
$$4 \div 4 = 1$$
$$6 \div 3 = 2$$
$$20 \div 5 = 4$$
$$18 \div 3 = 6$$
$$10 \div 5 = 2$$
$$15 \div 5 = 3$$
$$12 \div 4 = 3$$
$$12 \div 2 = 6$$

ANSWERS
Maths Minute 14

Andrew Brodie Publications
© A & C Black Publishers Ltd.

◆ Name	● Name	▲ Name	✴ Name
Division within 6,7,8 and 9 x tables	**Division within 6,7,8 and 9 x tables**	**Division within 6,7,8 and 9 x tables**	**Division within 6,7,8 and 9 x tables**
$21 \div 7 =$	$42 \div 6 =$	$63 \div 7 =$	$60 \div 6 =$
$40 \div 8 =$	$80 \div 8 =$	$6 \div 6 =$	$21 \div 7 =$
$6 \div 6 =$	$45 \div 9 =$	$16 \div 8 =$	$8 \div 8 =$
$45 \div 9 =$	$7 \div 7 =$	$14 \div 7 =$	$9 \div 9 =$
$54 \div 9 =$	$63 \div 9 =$	$27 \div 9 =$	$12 \div 6 =$
$28 \div 7 =$	$72 \div 8 =$	$24 \div 6 =$	$24 \div 8 =$
$48 \div 8 =$	$21 \div 7 =$	$80 \div 8 =$	$28 \div 7 =$
$48 \div 6 =$	$27 \div 9 =$	$7 \div 7 =$	$18 \div 9 =$
$18 \div 9 =$	$8 \div 8 =$	$81 \div 9 =$	$18 \div 6 =$
$35 \div 7 =$	$14 \div 7 =$	$18 \div 6 =$	$72 \div 8 =$
$18 \div 6 =$	$72 \div 9 =$	$32 \div 8 =$	$35 \div 7 =$
$72 \div 8 =$	$12 \div 6 =$	$45 \div 9 =$	$90 \div 9 =$
$80 \div 8 =$	$32 \div 8 =$	$56 \div 7 =$	$72 \div 9 =$
$42 \div 7 =$	$70 \div 7 =$	$90 \div 9 =$	$54 \div 6 =$
$54 \div 6 =$	$81 \div 9 =$	$56 \div 8 =$	$36 \div 6 =$
$81 \div 9 =$	$54 \div 6 =$	$30 \div 6 =$	$56 \div 8 =$
$56 \div 8 =$	$24 \div 8 =$	$63 \div 9 =$	$42 \div 7 =$
$24 \div 6 =$	$9 \div 9 =$	$49 \div 7 =$	$45 \div 9 =$
$90 \div 9 =$	$60 \div 6 =$	$48 \div 8 =$	$40 \div 8 =$
$49 \div 7 =$	$56 \div 7 =$	$42 \div 6 =$	$42 \div 6 =$
$36 \div 6 =$	$16 \div 8 =$	$54 \div 9 =$	$70 \div 7 =$
$9 \div 9 =$	$30 \div 6 =$	$64 \div 8 =$	$81 \div 9 =$
$64 \div 8 =$	$63 \div 7 =$	$48 \div 6 =$	$80 \div 8 =$
$70 \div 7 =$	$36 \div 6 =$	$70 \div 7 =$	$63 \div 7 =$
Maths Minute 15	**Maths Minute 15**	**Maths Minute 15**	**Maths Minute 15**

Andrew Brodie Publications
© A & C Black Publishers Ltd.   Andrew Brodie Publications
© A & C Black Publishers Ltd.   Andrew Brodie Publications
© A & C Black Publishers Ltd.   Andrew Brodie Publications
© A & C Black Publishers Ltd.

◆ ANSWERS
Division within 6, 7, 8 and 9 x tables

21 ÷ 7 =	3
40 ÷ 8 =	5
6 ÷ 6 =	1
45 ÷ 9 =	5
54 ÷ 9 =	6
28 ÷ 7 =	4
48 ÷ 8 =	6
48 ÷ 6 =	8
18 ÷ 9 =	2
35 ÷ 7 =	5
18 ÷ 6 =	3
72 ÷ 8 =	9
80 ÷ 8 =	10
42 ÷ 7 =	6
54 ÷ 6 =	9
81 ÷ 9 =	9
56 ÷ 8 =	7
24 ÷ 6 =	4
90 ÷ 9 =	10
49 ÷ 7 =	7
36 ÷ 6 =	6
9 ÷ 9 =	1
64 ÷ 8 =	8
70 ÷ 7 =	10

ANSWERS

Maths Minute 15

Andrew Brodie Publications
© A & C Black Publishers Ltd.

● ANSWERS
Division within 6, 7, 8 and 9 x tables

42 ÷ 6 =	7
80 ÷ 8 =	10
45 ÷ 9 =	5
7 ÷ 7 =	1
63 ÷ 9 =	7
72 ÷ 8 =	9
21 ÷ 7 =	3
27 ÷ 9 =	3
8 ÷ 8 =	1
14 ÷ 7 =	2
72 ÷ 9 =	8
12 ÷ 6 =	2
32 ÷ 8 =	4
70 ÷ 7 =	10
81 ÷ 9 =	9
54 ÷ 6 =	9
24 ÷ 8 =	3
9 ÷ 9 =	1
60 ÷ 6 =	10
56 ÷ 7 =	8
16 ÷ 8 =	2
30 ÷ 6 =	5
63 ÷ 7 =	9
36 ÷ 6 =	6

ANSWERS

Maths Minute 15

Andrew Brodie Publications
© A & C Black Publishers Ltd.

▲ ANSWERS
Division within 6, 7, 8 and 9 x tables

63 ÷ 7 =	9
6 ÷ 6 =	1
16 ÷ 8 =	2
14 ÷ 7 =	2
27 ÷ 9 =	3
24 ÷ 6 =	4
80 ÷ 8 =	10
7 ÷ 7 =	1
81 ÷ 9 =	9
18 ÷ 6 =	3
32 ÷ 8 =	4
45 ÷ 9 =	5
56 ÷ 7 =	8
90 ÷ 9 =	10
56 ÷ 8 =	7
30 ÷ 6 =	5
63 ÷ 9 =	7
49 ÷ 7 =	7
48 ÷ 8 =	6
42 ÷ 6 =	7
54 ÷ 9 =	6
64 ÷ 8 =	8
48 ÷ 6 =	8
70 ÷ 7 =	10

ANSWERS

Maths Minute 15

Andrew Brodie Publications
© A & C Black Publishers Ltd.

✴ ANSWERS
Division within 6, 7, 8 and 9 x tables

60 ÷ 6 =	10
21 ÷ 7 =	3
8 ÷ 8 =	1
9 ÷ 9 =	1
12 ÷ 6 =	2
24 ÷ 8 =	3
28 ÷ 7 =	4
18 ÷ 9 =	2
18 ÷ 6 =	3
72 ÷ 8 =	9
35 ÷ 7 =	5
90 ÷ 9 =	10
72 ÷ 9 =	8
54 ÷ 6 =	9
36 ÷ 6 =	6
56 ÷ 8 =	7
42 ÷ 7 =	6
45 ÷ 9 =	5
40 ÷ 8 =	5
42 ÷ 6 =	7
70 ÷ 7 =	10
81 ÷ 9 =	9
80 ÷ 8 =	10
63 ÷ 7 =	9

ANSWERS

Maths Minute 15

Andrew Brodie Publications
© A & C Black Publishers Ltd.

◆ Name	● Name	▲ Name	✳ Name
Multiplying by 10	Multiplying by 10	Multiplying by 10	Multiplying by 10
6 x 10 =	3 x 10 =	7 x 10 =	5 x 10 =
8 x 10 =	7 x 10 =	5 x 10 =	9 x 10 =
7 x 10 =	5 x 10 =	6 x 10 =	8 x 10 =
4 x 10 =	4 x 10 =	3 x 10 =	2 x 10 =
9 x 10 =	1 x 10 =	1 x 10 =	3 x 10 =
2 x 10 =	9 x 10 =	8 x 10 =	6 x 10 =
45 x 10 =	10 x 10 =	11 x 10 =	27 x 10 =
63 x 10 =	36 x 10 =	81 x 10 =	59 x 10 =
29 x 10 =	42 x 10 =	17 x 10 =	98 x 10 =
82 x 10 =	59 x 10 =	54 x 10 =	76 x 10 =
76 x 10 =	61 x 10 =	26 x 10 =	53 x 10 =
50 x 10 =	85 x 10 =	39 x 10 =	49 x 10 =
8 x 10 =	7 x 10 =	4 x 10 =	2 x 10 =
88 x 10 =	77 x 10 =	44 x 10 =	22 x 10 =
8·8 x 10 =	7·7 x 10 =	4·4 x 10 =	2·2 x 10 =
6 x 10 =	4 x 10 =	6 x 10 =	3 x 10 =
26 x 10 =	34 x 10 =	26 x 10 =	53 x 10 =
2·6 x 10 =	3·4 x 10 =	2·6 x 10 =	5·3 x 10 =
5 x 10 =	9 x 10 =	8 x 10 =	8 x 10 =
35 x 10 =	69 x 10 =	48 x 10 =	28 x 10 =
3·5 x 10 =	6·9 x 10 =	4·8 x 10 =	2·8 x 10 =
7 x 10 =	3 x 10 =	1 x 10 =	5 x 10 =
47 x 10 =	73 x 10 =	31 x 10 =	45 x 10 =
4·7 x 10 =	7·3 x 10 =	3·1 x 10 =	4·5 x 10 =

Maths Minute 16

Andrew Brodie Publications

◆ ANSWERS Multiplying by 10	● ANSWERS Multiplying by 10	▲ ANSWERS Multiplying by 10	✶ ANSWERS Multiplying by 10
6 x 10 = 60	3 x 10 = 30	7 x 10 = 70	5 x 10 = 50
8 x 10 = 80	7 x 10 = 70	5 x 10 = 50	9 x 10 = 90
7 x 10 = 70	5 x 10 = 50	6 x 10 = 60	8 x 10 = 80
4 x 10 = 40	4 x 10 = 40	3 x 10 = 30	2 x 10 = 20
9 x 10 = 90	1 x 10 = 10	1 x 10 = 10	3 x 10 = 30
2 x 10 = 20	9 x 10 = 90	8 x 10 = 80	6 x 10 = 60
45 x 10 = 450	10 x 10 = 100	11 x 10 = 110	27 x 10 = 270
63 x 10 = 630	36 x 10 = 360	81 x 10 = 810	59 x 10 = 590
29 x 10 = 290	42 x 10 = 420	17 x 10 = 170	98 x 10 = 980
82 x 10 = 820	59 x 10 = 590	54 x 10 = 540	76 x 10 = 760
76 x 10 = 760	61 x 10 = 610	26 x 10 = 260	53 x 10 = 530
50 x 10 = 500	85 x 10 = 850	39 x 10 = 390	49 x 10 = 490
8 x 10 = 80	7 x 10 = 70	4 x 10 = 40	2 x 10 = 20
88 x 10 = 880	77 x 10 = 770	44 x 10 = 440	22 x 10 = 220
8·8 x 10 = 88	7·7 x 10 = 77	4·4 x 10 = 44	2·2 x 10 = 22
6 x 10 = 60	4 x 10 = 40	6 x 10 = 60	3 x 10 = 30
26 x 10 = 260	34 x 10 = 340	26 x 10 = 260	53 x 10 = 530
2·6 x 10 = 26	3·4 x 10 = 34	2·6 x 10 = 26	5·3 x 10 = 53
5 x 10 = 50	9 x 10 = 90	8 x 10 = 80	8 x 10 = 80
35 x 10 = 350	69 x 10 = 690	48 x 10 = 480	28 x 10 = 280
3·5 x 10 = 35	6·9 x 10 = 69	4·8 x 10 = 48	2·8 x 10 = 28
7 x 10 = 70	3 x 10 = 30	1 x 10 = 10	5 x 10 = 50
47 x 10 = 470	73 x 10 = 730	31 x 10 = 310	45 x 10 = 450
4·7 x 10 = 47	7·3 x 10 = 73	3·1 x 10 = 31	4·5 x 10 = 45

Andrew Brodie Publications
© A & C Black Publishers Ltd.

◆ Name	● Name	▲ Name	✳ Name
2 digit multiples of 10 X 2,3,4,5,6,7,8 & 9	2 digit multiples of 10 X 2,3,4,5,6,7,8 & 9	2 digit multiples of 10 X 2,3,4,5,6,7,8 & 9	2 digit multiples of 10 X 2,3,4,5,6,7,8 & 9
40 x 2 =	10 x 3 =	20 x 4 =	90 x 2 =
30 x 5 =	20 x 5 =	10 x 7 =	30 x 7 =
80 x 8 =	40 x 2 =	20 x 8 =	10 x 4 =
60 x 4 =	70 x 7 =	60 x 7 =	20 x 6 =
10 x 3 =	60 x 8 =	60 x 4 =	40 x 6 =
50 x 7 =	30 x 5 =	90 x 8 =	10 x 8 =
30 x 6 =	40 x 7 =	60 x 6 =	20 x 4 =
40 x 6 =	90 x 3 =	10 x 2 =	60 x 8 =
70 x 8 =	70 x 6 =	70 x 6 =	70 x 2 =
20 x 4 =	60 x 2 =	30 x 3 =	80 x 8 =
60 x 5 =	20 x 9 =	50 x 6 =	60 x 4 =
10 x 9 =	50 x 4 =	80 x 4 =	90 x 9 =
50 x 5 =	90 x 8 =	60 x 5 =	90 x 5 =
90 x 8 =	80 x 5 =	90 x 7 =	60 x 2 =
90 x 3 =	20 x 2 =	40 x 2 =	30 x 5 =
30 x 3 =	50 x 7 =	30 x 8 =	10 x 9 =
70 x 7 =	60 x 4 =	70 x 3 =	30 x 3 =
60 x 9 =	40 x 9 =	30 x 5 =	60 x 6 =
80 x 7 =	70 x 3 =	70 x 9 =	70 x 7 =
20 x 2 =	30 x 9 =	80 x 2 =	70 x 5 =
90 x 6 =	40 x 8 =	60 x 9 =	50 x 3 =
40 x 8 =	20 x 6 =	10 x 5 =	30 x 9 =
70 x 9 =	30 x 6 =	90 x 3 =	50 x 7 =
20 x 6 =	80 x 4 =	30 x 9 =	60 x 3 =

Maths Minute 17

Andrew Brodie Publications
© A & C Black Publishers Ltd.

Maths Minute 17

Andrew Brodie Publications
© A & C Black Publishers Ltd.

Maths Minute 17

Andrew Brodie Publications
© A & C Black Publishers Ltd.

Maths Minute 17

Andrew Brodie Publications
© A & C Black Publishers Ltd.

◆ ANSWERS

2 digit multiples of 10 X 2,3,4,5,6,7,8 & 9

40 x 2 = 80

30 x 5 = 150

80 x 8 = 640

60 x 4 = 240

10 x 3 = 30

50 x 7 = 350

30 x 6 = 180

40 x 6 = 240

70 x 8 = 560

20 x 4 = 80

60 x 5 = 300

10 x 9 = 90

50 x 5 = 250

90 x 8 = 720

90 x 3 = 270

30 x 3 = 90

70 x 7 = 490

60 x 9 = 540

80 x 7 = 560

20 x 2 = 40

90 x 6 = 540

40 x 8 = 320

70 x 9 = 630

20 x 6 = 120

ANSWERS

Maths Minute 17

Andrew Brodie Publications

● ANSWERS

2 digit multiples of 10 X 2,3,4,5,6,7,8 & 9

10 x 3 = 30

20 x 5 = 100

40 x 2 = 80

70 x 7 = 490

60 x 8 = 480

30 x 5 = 150

40 x 7 = 280

90 x 3 = 270

70 x 6 = 420

60 x 2 = 120

20 x 9 = 180

50 x 4 = 200

90 x 8 = 720

80 x 5 = 400

20 x 2 = 40

50 x 7 = 350

60 x 4 = 240

40 x 9 = 360

70 x 3 = 210

30 x 9 = 270

40 x 8 = 320

20 x 6 = 120

30 x 6 = 180

80 x 4 = 320

ANSWERS

Maths Minute 17

Andrew Brodie Publications

▲ ANSWERS

2 digit multiples of 10 X 2,3,4,5,6,7,8 & 9

20 x 4 = 80

10 x 7 = 70

20 x 8 = 160

60 x 7 = 420

60 x 4 = 240

90 x 8 = 720

60 x 6 = 360

10 x 2 = 20

70 x 6 = 420

30 x 3 = 90

50 x 6 = 300

80 x 4 = 320

60 x 5 = 300

90 x 7 = 630

40 x 2 = 80

30 x 8 = 240

70 x 3 = 210

30 x 5 = 150

70 x 9 = 630

80 x 2 = 160

60 x 9 = 540

10 x 5 = 50

90 x 3 = 270

30 x 9 = 270

ANSWERS

Maths Minute 17

Andrew Brodie Publications

✸ ANSWERS

2 digit multiples of 10 X 2,3,4,5,6,7,8 & 9

90 x 2 = 180

30 x 7 = 210

10 x 4 = 40

20 x 6 = 120

40 x 6 = 240

10 x 8 = 80

20 x 4 = 80

60 x 8 = 480

70 x 2 = 140

80 x 8 = 640

60 x 4 = 240

90 x 9 = 810

90 x 5 = 450

60 x 2 = 120

30 x 5 = 150

10 x 9 = 90

30 x 3 = 90

60 x 6 = 360

70 x 7 = 490

70 x 5 = 350

50 x 3 = 150

30 x 9 = 270

50 x 7 = 350

60 x 3 = 180

ANSWERS

Maths Minute 17

Andrew Brodie Publications

◆ Name	● Name	▲ Name	✳ Name
X 10 including decimals	X 10 including decimals	X 10 including decimals	X 10 including decimals
2.4 x 10 =	8.3 x 10 =	5.5 x 10 =	3.3 x 10 =
8.6 x 10 =	2.9 x 10 =	6.7 x 10 =	6.8 x 10 =
9.5 x 10 =	6.8 x 10 =	2.4 x 10 =	5.1 x 10 =
4.8 x 10 =	0.4 x 10 =	8.9 x 10 =	4.9 x 10 =
0.6 x 10 =	4.4 x 10 =	0.7 x 10 =	8.7 x 10 =
24.8 x 10 =	27.3 x 10 =	36.1 x 10 =	38.1 x 10 =
42.8 x 10 =	82.1 x 10 =	42.6 x 10 =	46.4 x 10 =
28 x 10 =	82 x 10 =	93.9 x 10 =	83.9 x 10 =
6 x 10 =	37 x 10 =	84 x 10 =	3.9 x 10 =
36.9 x 10 =	3.7 x 10 =	8.6 x 10 =	390 x 10 =
94.1 x 10 =	370 x 10 =	84.1 x 10 =	39.9 x 10 =
20.3 x 10 =	64 x 10 =	4.1 x 10 =	84 x 10 =
203 x 10 =	0.9 x 10 =	0.8 x 10 =	47.7 x 10 =
9.9 x 10 =	9.8 x 10 =	72 x 10 =	65.2 x 10 =
96 x 10 =	6.1 x 10 =	7.2 x 10 =	84.8 x 10 =
42 x 10 =	0.7 x 10 =	72.4 x 10 =	4.8 x 10 =
0.5 x 10 =	61.3 x 10 =	60 x 10 =	848 x 10 =
50.5 x 10 =	72.1 x 10 =	6 x 10 =	8.4 x 10 =
5.5 x 10 =	21.2 x 10 =	0.6 x 10 =	2.6 x 10 =
40.2 x 10 =	12 x 10 =	60.2 x 10 =	26 x 10 =
0.7 x 10 =	122 x 10 =	602 x 10 =	53 x 10 =
3.8 x 10 =	12.1 x 10 =	237 x 10 =	981 x 10 =
46 x 10 =	91 x 10 =	0.3 x 10 =	0.4 x 10 =
8.4 x 10 =	7.6 x 10 =	5.1 x 10 =	7.2 x 10 =

Maths Minute 18 | **Maths Minute 18** | **Maths Minute 18** | **Maths Minute 18**

Andrew Brodie Publications
© A & C Black Publishers Ltd.   Andrew Brodie Publications
© A & C Black Publishers Ltd.   Andrew Brodie Publications
© A & C Black Publishers Ltd.   Andrew Brodie Publications
© A & C Black Publishers Ltd.

◆ ANSWERS

X 10 including decimals

2.4 x 10 =	24
8.6 x 10 =	86
9.5 x 10 =	95
4.8 x 10 =	48
0.6 x 10 =	6
24.8 x 10 =	248
42.8 x 10 =	428
28 x 10 =	280
6 x 10 =	60
36.9 x 10 =	369
94.1 x 10 =	941
20.3 x 10 =	203
203 x 10 =	2030
9.9 x 10 =	99
96 x 10 =	960
42 x 10 =	420
0.5 x 10 =	5
50.5 x 10 =	505
5.5 x 10 =	55
40.2 x 10 =	402
0.7 x 10 =	7
3.8 x 10 =	38
46 x 10 =	46
8.4 x 10 =	84

ANSWERS

Maths Minute 18

Andrew Brodie Publications
© A & C Black Publishers Ltd.

● ANSWERS

X 10 including decimals

8.3 x 10 =	83
2.9 x 10 =	29
6.8 x 10 =	68
0.4 x 10 =	4
4.4 x 10 =	44
27.3 x 10 =	273
82.1 x 10 =	821
82 x 10 =	820
37 x 10 =	370
3.7 x 10 =	37
370 x 10 =	3700
64 x 10 =	640
0.9 x 10 =	9
9.8 x 10 =	98
6.1 x 10 =	61
0.7 x 10 =	7
61.3 x 10 =	613
72.1 x 10 =	721
21.2 x 10 =	212
12 x 10 =	120
122 x 10 =	1220
12.1 x 10 =	121
91 x 10 =	910
7.6 x 10 =	76

ANSWERS

Maths Minute 18

Andrew Brodie Publications
© A & C Black Publishers Ltd.

▲ ANSWERS

X 10 including decimals

5.5 x 10 =	55
6.7 x 10 =	67
2.4 x 10 =	24
8.9 x 10 =	89
0.7 x 10 =	7
36.1 x 10 =	361
42.6 x 10 =	426
93.9 x 10 =	939
84 x 10 =	840
8.6 x 10 =	86
84.1 x 10 =	841
4.1 x 10 =	41
0.8 x 10 =	8
72 x 10 =	720
7.2 x 10 =	72
72.4 x 10 =	724
60 x 10 =	600
6 x 10 =	60
0.6 x 10 =	6
60.2 x 10 =	602
602 x 10 =	6020
237 x 10 =	2370
0.3 x 10 =	3
5.1 x 10 =	51

ANSWERS

Maths Minute 18

Andrew Brodie Publications
© A & C Black Publishers Ltd.

✸ ANSWERS

X 10 including decimals

3.3 x 10 =	33
6.8 x 10 =	68
5.1 x 10 =	51
4.9 x 10 =	49
8.7 x 10 =	87
38.1 x 10 =	381
46.4 x 10 =	464
83.9 x 10 =	839
3.9 x 10 =	39
390 x 10 =	3900
39.9 x 10 =	399
84 x 10 =	840
47.7 x 10 =	477
65.2 x 10 =	652
84.8 x 10 =	848
4.8 x 10 =	48
848 x 10 =	8480
8.4 x 10 =	84
2.6 x 10 =	26
26 x 10 =	260
53 x 10 =	530
981 x 10 =	9810
0.4 x 10 =	4
7.2 x 10 =	72

ANSWERS

Maths Minute 18

Andrew Brodie Publications
© A & C Black Publishers Ltd.

◆ Name	● Name	▲ Name	✳ Name
Insert more than > or less than <	**Insert more than >** or less than <	**Insert more than >** or less than <	**Insert more than >** or less than <
6 ☐ 8	3 ☐ 7	1 ☐ 11	5 ☐ 4
5 ☐ 15	8 ☐ 6	2 ☐ 1	1 ☐ 13
13 ☐ 12	11 ☐ 21	7 ☐ 4	10 ☐ 11
14 ☐ 8	17 ☐ 6	9 ☐ 8	23 ☐ 29
23 ☐ 26	23 ☐ 32	10 ☐ 12	151 ☐ 51
11 ☐ 12	41 ☐ 46	37 ☐ 39	63 ☐ 67
13 ☐ 31	16 ☐ 61	56 ☐ 28	29 ☐ 31
151 ☐ 115	127 ☐ 172	33 ☐ 44	99 ☐ 100
372 ☐ 369	324 ☐ 327	29 ☐ 92	173 ☐ 371
281 ☐ 273	64 ☐ 43	124 ☐ 139	274 ☐ 247
199 ☐ 119	391 ☐ 319	183 ☐ 381	282 ☐ 323
267 ☐ 134	421 ☐ 199	319 ☐ 391	333 ☐ 344
17 ☐ 71	898 ☐ 799	770 ☐ 769	899 ☐ 700
36 ☐ 360	697 ☐ 703	630 ☐ 139	460 ☐ 390
59 ☐ 109	401 ☐ 410	910 ☐ 901	999 ☐ 1000
370 ☐ 307	624 ☐ 426	237 ☐ 739	481 ☐ 184
333 ☐ 399	501 ☐ 499	199 ☐ 911	677 ☐ 777
123 ☐ 321	789 ☐ 987	799 ☐ 800	191 ☐ 919
$1\frac{1}{2}$ ☐ 0·5	0·5 ☐ 1	$\frac{1}{2}$ ☐ $\frac{1}{4}$	0·5 ☐ 2
0·5 ☐ 50	1·5 ☐ 1	2 ☐ $\frac{3}{4}$	$\frac{1}{2}$ ☐ 1
$\frac{1}{2}$ ☐ 1	2 ☐ $\frac{1}{2}$	0·5 ☐ 0·75	0·75 ☐ $\frac{9}{10}$
0·75 ☐ 1	2 ☐ 0·75	$\frac{3}{4}$ ☐ $\frac{1}{4}$	$\frac{3}{4}$ ☐ $\frac{1}{2}$
$\frac{1}{2}$ ☐ $\frac{3}{4}$	$\frac{1}{2}$ ☐ $\frac{1}{4}$	$\frac{1}{4}$ ☐ $\frac{1}{10}$	$\frac{1}{4}$ ☐ 0·75
$\frac{1}{2}$ ☐ $\frac{1}{4}$	$\frac{3}{4}$ ☐ $\frac{1}{10}$	$\frac{1}{4}$ ☐ $\frac{9}{10}$	0·25 ☐ 0·5
Maths Minute 19	**Maths Minute 19**	**Maths Minute 19**	**Maths Minute 19**

Andrew Brodie Publications © A & C Black Publishers Ltd.   Andrew Brodie Publications © A & C Black Publishers Ltd.   Andrew Brodie Publications © A & C Black Publishers Ltd.   Andrew Brodie Publications © A & C Black Publishers Ltd.

Column 1 — ◆ ANSWERS

Insert more than >
or less than <

6	<	8
5	<	15
13	>	12
14	>	8
23	<	26
11	<	12
13	<	31
151	>	115
372	>	369
281	>	273
199	>	119
267	>	134
17	<	71
36	<	360
59	<	109
370	>	307
333	<	399
123	<	321
$1\frac{1}{2}$	>	0·5
0·5	<	50
$\frac{1}{2}$	<	1
0·75	<	1
$\frac{1}{2}$	<	$\frac{3}{4}$
$\frac{1}{2}$	>	$\frac{1}{4}$

ANSWERS

Maths Minute 19

Andrew Brodie Publications
© A & C Black Publishers Ltd.

Column 2 — ● ANSWERS

Insert more than >
or less than <

3	<	7
8	>	6
11	<	21
17	>	6
23	<	32
41	<	46
16	<	61
127	<	172
324	<	327
64	>	43
391	>	319
421	>	199
898	>	799
697	<	703
401	<	410
624	>	426
501	>	499
789	<	987
0·5	<	1
1·5	>	1
2	>	$\frac{1}{2}$
2	>	0·75
$\frac{1}{2}$	>	$\frac{1}{4}$
$\frac{3}{4}$	>	$\frac{1}{10}$

ANSWERS

Maths Minute 19

Andrew Brodie Publications
© A & C Black Publishers Ltd.

Column 3 — ▲ ANSWERS

Insert more than >
or less than <

1	<	11
2	>	1
7	>	4
9	>	8
10	<	12
37	<	39
56	>	28
33	<	44
29	<	92
124	<	139
183	<	381
319	<	391
770	>	769
630	>	139
910	>	901
237	<	739
199	<	911
799	<	800
$\frac{1}{2}$	>	$\frac{1}{4}$
2	>	$\frac{3}{4}$
0·5	<	0·75
$\frac{3}{4}$	>	$\frac{1}{4}$
$\frac{1}{4}$	>	$\frac{1}{10}$
$\frac{1}{4}$	<	$\frac{9}{10}$

ANSWERS

Maths Minute 19

Andrew Brodie Publications
© A & C Black Publishers Ltd.

Column 4 — ✸ ANSWERS

Insert more than >
or less than <

5	>	4
1	<	13
10	<	11
23	<	29
151	>	51
63	<	67
29	<	31
99	<	100
173	<	371
274	>	247
282	<	323
333	<	344
899	>	700
460	>	390
999	<	1000
481	>	184
677	<	777
191	<	919
0·5	<	2
$\frac{1}{2}$	<	1
0·75	<	$\frac{9}{10}$
$\frac{3}{4}$	>	$\frac{1}{2}$
$\frac{1}{4}$	<	0·75
0·25	<	0·5

ANSWERS

Maths Minute 19

Andrew Brodie Publications
© A & C Black Publishers Ltd.

◆ Name	● Name	▲ Name	✴ Name
Square numbers	Square numbers	Square numbers	Square numbers
$2^2 =$	$1^2 =$	$10^2 =$	$4^2 =$
$3^2 =$	$2^2 =$	$9^2 =$	$5^2 =$
$7^2 =$	$3^2 =$	$8^2 =$	$9^2 =$
$8^2 =$	$4^2 =$	$7^2 =$	$1^2 =$
$9^2 =$	$5^2 =$	$6^2 =$	$8^2 =$
$4^2 =$	$6^2 =$	$5^2 =$	$6^2 =$
$1^2 =$	$7^2 =$	$4^2 =$	$7^2 =$
$10^2 =$	$8^2 =$	$3^2 =$	$3^2 =$
$5^2 =$	$9^2 =$	$2^2 =$	$10^2 =$
$6^2 =$	$10^2 =$	$1^2 =$	$2^2 =$
$20^2 =$	$30^2 =$	$40^2 =$	$50^2 =$
$7^2 + 2^2 =$	$5^2 + 5^2 =$	$8^2 + 1^2 =$	$8^2 + 5^2 =$
$6^2 + 3^2 =$	$8^2 + 1^2 =$	$4^2 + 2^2 =$	$9^2 + 1^2 =$
$2^2 + 1^2 =$	$6^2 + 2^2 =$	$3^2 + 5^2 =$	$6^2 + 3^2 =$
$4^2 + 2^2 =$	$3^2 + 5^2 =$	$5^2 + 1^2 =$	$4^2 + 5^2 =$
$8^2 + 1^2 =$	$4^2 + 2^2 =$	$7^2 + 2^2 =$	$3^2 + 3^2 =$
$2^2 + 2^2 =$	$1^2 + 6^2 =$	$2^2 + 7^2 =$	$5^2 + 8^2 =$
$4^2 + 4^2 =$	$9^2 + 3^2 =$	$6^2 + 3^2 =$	$7^2 + 6^2 =$
$4^2 - 2^2 =$	$5^2 - 5^2 =$	$9^2 - 6^2 =$	$8^2 - 2^2 =$
$6^2 - 1^2 =$	$6^2 - 2^2 =$	$4^2 - 1^2 =$	$9^2 - 5^2 =$
$3^2 - 2^2 =$	$3^2 - 1^2 =$	$3^2 - 3^2 =$	$4^2 - 1^2 =$
$8^2 - 8^2 =$	$4^2 - 2^2 =$	$9^2 - 3^2 =$	$6^2 - 3^2 =$
$9^2 - 6^2 =$	$8^2 - 7^2 =$	$7^2 - 5^2 =$	$7^2 - 4^2 =$
$10^2 - 5^2 =$	$7^2 - 5^2 =$	$4^2 - 1^2 =$	$7^2 - 6^2 =$
Maths Minute 20	**Maths Minute 20**	**Maths Minute 20**	**Maths Minute 20**

Andrew Brodie Publications © A & C Black Publishers Ltd. Andrew Brodie Publications © A & C Black Publishers Ltd. Andrew Brodie Publications © A & C Black Publishers Ltd. Andrew Brodie Publications © A & C Black Publishers Ltd.

◆	●	▲	✶
$2^2 = 4$	$1^2 = 1$	$10^2 = 100$	$4^2 = 16$
$3^2 = 9$	$2^2 = 4$	$9^2 = 81$	$5^2 = 25$
$7^2 = 49$	$3^2 = 9$	$8^2 = 64$	$9^2 = 81$
$8^2 = 64$	$4^2 = 16$	$7^2 = 49$	$1^2 = 1$
$9^2 = 81$	$5^2 = 25$	$6^2 = 36$	$8^2 = 64$
$4^2 = 16$	$6^2 = 36$	$5^2 = 25$	$6^2 = 36$
$1^2 = 1$	$7^2 = 49$	$4^2 = 16$	$7^2 = 49$
$10^2 = 100$	$8^2 = 64$	$3^2 = 9$	$3^2 = 9$
$5^2 = 25$	$9^2 = 81$	$2^2 = 4$	$10^2 = 100$
$6^2 = 36$	$10^2 = 100$	$1^2 = 1$	$2^2 = 4$
$20^2 = 400$	$30^2 = 900$	$40^2 = 1600$	$50^2 = 2500$
$7^2 + 2^2 = 53$	$5^2 + 5^2 = 50$	$8^2 + 1^2 = 65$	$8^2 + 5^2 = 89$
$6^2 + 3^2 = 45$	$8^2 + 1^2 = 65$	$4^2 + 2^2 = 20$	$9^2 + 1^2 = 82$
$2^2 + 1^2 = 5$	$6^2 + 2^2 = 40$	$3^2 + 5^2 = 34$	$6^2 + 3^2 = 45$
$4^2 + 2^2 = 20$	$3^2 + 5^2 = 34$	$5^2 + 1^2 = 26$	$4^2 + 5^2 = 41$
$8^2 + 1^2 = 65$	$4^2 + 2^2 = 20$	$7^2 + 2^2 = 53$	$3^2 + 3^2 = 18$
$2^2 + 2^2 = 8$	$1^2 + 6^2 = 37$	$2^2 + 7^2 = 53$	$5^2 + 8^2 = 89$
$4^2 + 4^2 = 32$	$9^2 + 3^2 = 90$	$6^2 + 3^2 = 45$	$7^2 + 6^2 = 85$
$4^2 - 2^2 = 12$	$5^2 - 5^2 = 0$	$9^2 - 6^2 = 45$	$8^2 - 2^2 = 60$
$6^2 - 1^2 = 35$	$6^2 - 2^2 = 32$	$4^2 - 1^2 = 15$	$9^2 - 5^2 = 56$
$3^2 - 2^2 = 5$	$3^2 - 1^2 = 8$	$3^2 - 3^2 = 0$	$4^2 - 1^2 = 15$
$8^2 - 8^2 = 0$	$4^2 - 2^2 = 12$	$9^2 - 3^2 = 72$	$6^2 - 3^2 = 27$
$9^2 - 6^2 = 45$	$8^2 - 7^2 = 15$	$7^2 - 5^2 = 24$	$7^2 - 4^2 = 33$
$10^2 - 5^2 = 75$	$7^2 - 5^2 = 24$	$4^2 - 1^2 = 15$	$7^2 - 6^2 = 13$

ANSWERS	**ANSWERS**	**ANSWERS**	**ANSWERS**
Maths Minute 20	**Maths Minute 20**	**Maths Minute 20**	**Maths Minute 20**
Andrew Brodie Publications	Andrew Brodie Publications	Andrew Brodie Publications	Andrew Brodie Publications
© A & C Black Publishers Ltd.	© A & C Black Publishers Ltd.	© A & C Black Publishers Ltd.	© A & C Black Publishers Ltd.

◆ Name	● Name	▲ Name	✳ Name
Double these numbers	Double these numbers	Double these numbers	Double these numbers
Double 230 =	Double 110 =	Double 240 =	Double 120 =
Double 250 =	Double 920 =	Double 960 =	Double 610 =
Double 700 =	Double 310 =	Double 440 =	Double 360 =
Double 120 =	Double 550 =	Double 630 =	Double 410 =
Double 720 =	Double 280 =	Double 120 =	Double 630 =
Double 310 =	Double 630 =	Double 130 =	Double 160 =
Double 110 =	Double 140 =	Double 610 =	Double 840 =
Double 690 =	Double 960 =	Double 560 =	Double 580 =
Double 340 =	Double 570 =	Double 380 =	Double 380 =
Double 260 =	Double 660 =	Double 910 =	Double 830 =
Double 430 =	Double 250 =	Double 260 =	Double 190 =
Double 750 =	Double 870 =	Double 890 =	Double 870 =
Double 320 =	Double 490 =	Double 450 =	Double 430 =
Double 980 =	Double 680 =	Double 150 =	Double 780 =
Double 560 =	Double 170 =	Double 860 =	Double 210 =
Double 360 =	Double 720 =	Double 520 =	Double 770 =
Double 630 =	Double 580 =	Double 290 =	Double 390 =
Double 920 =	Double 780 =	Double 710 =	Double 230 =
Double 450 =	Double 230 =	Double 480 =	Double 660 =
Double 860 =	Double 830 =	Double 340 =	Double 470 =

Maths Minute 21

Andrew Brodie Publications
© A & C Black Publishers Ltd.

Maths Minute 21

Andrew Brodie Publications
© A & C Black Publishers Ltd.

Maths Minute 21

Andrew Brodie Publications
© A & C Black Publishers Ltd.

Maths Minute 21

Andrew Brodie Publications
© A & C Black Publishers Ltd.

◆ ANSWERS	● ANSWERS	▲ ANSWERS	✳ ANSWERS
Double these numbers	*Double these numbers*	*Double these numbers*	*Double these numbers*
Double 230 = 460	Double 110 = 220	Double 240 = 480	Double 120 = 240
Double 250 = 500	Double 920 = 1840	Double 960 = 1920	Double 610 = 1220
Double 700 = 1400	Double 310 = 620	Double 440 = 880	Double 360 = 720
Double 120 = 240	Double 550 = 1100	Double 630 = 1260	Double 410 = 820
Double 720 = 1440	Double 280 = 560	Double 120 = 240	Double 630 = 1260
Double 310 = 620	Double 630 = 1260	Double 130 = 260	Double 160 = 320
Double 110 = 220	Double 140 = 280	Double 610 = 1220	Double 840 = 1680
Double 690 = 1380	Double 960 = 1920	Double 560 = 1120	Double 580 = 1160
Double 340 = 680	Double 570 = 1140	Double 380 = 760	Double 380 = 760
Double 260 = 520	Double 660 = 1320	Double 910 = 1820	Double 830 = 1660
Double 430 = 860	Double 250 = 500	Double 260 = 520	Double 190 = 380
Double 750 = 1500	Double 870 = 1740	Double 890 = 1780	Double 870 = 1740
Double 320 = 640	Double 490 = 980	Double 450 = 900	Double 430 = 860
Double 980 = 1960	Double 680 = 1360	Double 150 = 300	Double 780 = 1560
Double 560 = 1120	Double 170 = 340	Double 860 = 1720	Double 210 = 420
Double 360 = 720	Double 720 = 1440	Double 520 = 1040	Double 770 = 1540
Double 630 = 1260	Double 580 = 1160	Double 290 = 580	Double 390 = 780
Double 920 = 1840	Double 780 = 1560	Double 710 = 1420	Double 230 = 460
Double 450 = 900	Double 230 = 460	Double 480 = 960	Double 660 = 1320
Double 860 = 1720	Double 830 = 1660	Double 340 = 680	Double 470 = 940

ANSWERS	**ANSWERS**	**ANSWERS**	**ANSWERS**
Maths Minute 21	**Maths Minute 21**	**Maths Minute 21**	**Maths Minute 21**

Andrew Brodie Publications
© A & C Black Publishers Ltd. | Andrew Brodie Publications
© A & C Black Publishers Ltd. | Andrew Brodie Publications
© A & C Black Publishers Ltd. | Andrew Brodie Publications
© A & C Black Publishers Ltd.

◆ Name	● Name	▲ Name	✳ Name
25 X table	25 X table	25 X table	25 X table
1 x 25 =	1 x 25 =	4 x 25 =	3 x 25 =
8 x 25 =	8 x 25 =	3 x 25 =	8 x 25 =
2 x 25 =	10 x 25 =	10 x 25 =	4 x 25 =
10 x 25 =	9 x 25 =	5 x 25 =	9 x 25 =
9 x 25 =	2 x 25 =	8 x 25 =	5 x 25 =
6 x 25 =	7 x 25 =	2 x 25 =	10 x 25 =
4 x 25 =	4 x 25 =	6 x 25 =	12 x 25 =
5 x 25 =	6 x 25 =	7 x 25 =	16 x 25 =
7 x 25 =	3 x 25 =	9 x 25 =	6 x 25 =
3 x 25 =	5 x 25 =	1 x 25 =	24 x 25 =
20 x 25 =	20 x 25 =	40 x 25 =	28 x 25 =
70 x 25 =	80 x 25 =	70 x 25 =	32 x 25 =
30 x 25 =	30 x 25 =	20 x 25 =	36 x 25 =
60 x 25 =	50 x 25 =	50 x 25 =	20 x 25 =
50 x 25 =	90 x 25 =	30 x 25 =	50 x 25 =
25 ÷ 25 =	50 ÷ 25 =	75 ÷ 25 =	50 ÷ 25 =
75 ÷ 25 =	75 ÷ 25 =	100 ÷ 25 =	25 ÷ 25 =
150 ÷ 25 =	125 ÷ 25 =	200 ÷ 25 =	125 ÷ 25 =
125 ÷ 25 =	100 ÷ 25 =	250 ÷ 25 =	75 ÷ 25 =
175 ÷ 25 =	250 ÷ 25 =	175 ÷ 25 =	225 ÷ 25 =

Maths Minute 22

Andrew Brodie Publications
© A & C Black Publishers Ltd.

◆ ANSWERS	● ANSWERS	▲ ANSWERS	✳ ANSWERS
25 X table	25 X table	25 X table	25 X table
1 x 25 = 25	1 x 25 = 25	4 x 25 = 100	3 x 25 = 75
8 x 25 = 200	8 x 25 = 200	3 x 25 = 75	8 x 25 = 200
2 x 25 = 50	10 x 25 = 250	10 x 25 = 250	4 x 25 = 100
10 x 25 = 250	9 x 25 = 225	5 x 25 = 125	9 x 25 = 225
9 x 25 = 225	2 x 25 = 50	8 x 25 = 200	5 x 25 = 125
6 x 25 = 150	7 x 25 = 175	2 x 25 = 50	10 x 25 = 250
4 x 25 = 100	4 x 25 = 100	6 x 25 = 150	12 x 25 = 300
5 x 25 = 125	6 x 25 = 150	7 x 25 = 175	16 x 25 = 400
7 x 25 = 175	3 x 25 = 75	9 x 25 = 225	6 x 25 = 150
3 x 25 = 75	5 x 25 = 125	1 x 25 = 25	24 x 25 = 600
20 x 25 = 500	20 x 25 = 500	40 x 25 = 1000	28 x 25 = 700
70 x 25 = 1750	80 x 25 = 2000	70 x 25 = 1750	32 x 25 = 800
30 x 25 = 750	30 x 25 = 750	20 x 25 = 500	36 x 25 = 900
60 x 25 = 1500	50 x 25 = 1250	50 x 25 = 1250	20 x 25 = 500
50 x 25 = 1250	90 x 25 = 2250	30 x 25 = 750	50 x 25 = 1250
25 ÷ 25 = 1	50 ÷ 25 = 2	75 ÷ 25 = 3	50 ÷ 25 = 2
75 ÷ 25 = 3	75 ÷ 25 = 3	100 ÷ 25 = 4	25 ÷ 25 = 1
150 ÷ 25 = 6	125 ÷ 25 = 5	200 ÷ 25 = 8	125 ÷ 25 = 5
125 ÷ 25 = 5	100 ÷ 25 = 4	250 ÷ 25 = 10	75 ÷ 25 = 3
175 ÷ 25 = 7	250 ÷ 25 = 10	175 ÷ 25 = 7	225 ÷ 25 = 9

ANSWERS

Maths Minute 22

Andrew Brodie Publications
© A & C Black Publishers Ltd.

ANSWERS

Maths Minute 22

Andrew Brodie Publications
© A & C Black Publishers Ltd.

ANSWERS

Maths Minute 22

Andrew Brodie Publications
© A & C Black Publishers Ltd.

ANSWERS

Maths Minute 22

Andrew Brodie Publications
© A & C Black Publishers Ltd.

◆ Name	● Name	▲ Name
Calculate 50% of the following	Calculate 50% of the following	Calculate 50% of the following
50% of 100 =	50% of 90 =	50% of 60 =
50% of 96 =	50% of 28 =	50% of 36 =
50% of 22 =	50% of 58 =	50% of 48 =
50% of 56 =	50% of 86 =	50% of 84 =
50% of 98 =	50% of 34 =	50% of 66 =
50% of 46 =	50% of 62 =	50% of 44 =
50% of 222 =	50% of 286 =	50% of 248 =
50% of 256 =	50% of 234 =	50% of 284 =
50% of 298 =	50% of 262 =	50% of 244 =
50% of 408 =	50% of 600 =	50% of 800 =
50% of 76 =	50% of 98 =	50% of 96 =
50% of 84 =	50% of 18 =	50% of 16 =
50% of £0.48 =	50% of £0.36 =	50% of £0.24 =
50% of £0.74 =	50% of £0.88 =	50% of £0.12 =
50% of £0.12 =	50% of £0.92 =	50% of £0.16 =
50% of £0.62 =	50% of £0.76 =	50% of £0.38 =
50% of £4.22 =	50% of £0.54 =	50% of £0.54 =
50% of £6.84 =	50% of £6.28 =	50% of £6.28 =
50% of £2.76 =	50% of £4.84 =	50% of £4.64 =
50% of £8.36 =	50% of £2.48 =	50% of £2.82 =

Maths Minute 23

Andrew Brodie Publications
© A & C Black Publishers Ltd.

Maths Minute 23

Andrew Brodie Publications
© A & C Black Publishers Ltd.

Maths Minute 23

Andrew Brodie Publications
© A & C Black Publishers Ltd.

 **ANSWERS**

Calculate 50% of the following

50% of 100 = 50

50% of 96 = 48

50% of 22 = 11

50% of 56 = 28

50% of 98 = 49

50% of 46 = 23

50% of 222 = 111

50% of 256 = 128

50% of 298 = 149

50% of 408 = 204

50% of 76 = 38

50% of 84 = 42

50% of £0.48 = £0.24

50% of £0.74 = £0.37

50% of £0.12 = £0.06

50% of £0.62 = £0.31

50% of £4.22 = £2.11

50% of £6.84 = £3.42

50% of £2.76 = £1.38

50% of £8.36 = £4.18

ANSWERS

Maths Minute 23

Andrew Brodie Publications
© A & C Black Publishers Ltd.

● **ANSWERS**

Calculate 50% of the following

50% of 90 = 45

50% of 28 = 14

50% of 58 = 29

50% of 86 = 43

50% of 34 = 17

50% of 62 = 31

50% of 286 = 143

50% of 234 = 117

50% of 262 = 131

50% of 600 = 300

50% of 98 = 49

50% of 18 = 9

50% of £0.36 = £0.18

50% of £0.88 = £0.44

50% of £0.92 = £0.46

50% of £0.76 = £0.38

50% of £0.54 = £0.27

50% of £6.28 = £3.14

50% of £4.84 = £2.42

50% of £2.48 = £1.24

ANSWERS

Maths Minute 23

Andrew Brodie Publications
© A & C Black Publishers Ltd.

▲ **ANSWERS**

Calculate 50% of the following

50% of 60 = 30

50% of 36 = 18

50% of 48 = 24

50% of 84 = 42

50% of 66 = 33

50% of 44 = 22

50% of 248 = 124

50% of 284 = 142

50% of 244 = 122

50% of 800 = 400

50% of 96 = 48

50% of 16 = 8

50% of £0.24 = £0.12

50% of £0.12 = £0.06

50% of £0.16 = £0.08

50% of £0.38 = £0.19

50% of £0.54 = £0.27

50% of £6.28 = £3.14

50% of £4.64 = £2.32

50% of £2.82 = £1.41

ANSWERS

Maths Minute 23

Andrew Brodie Publications
© A & C Black Publishers Ltd.

 Name | ● Name | ▲ Name

Calculate 25% of the following	Calculate 25% of the following	Calculate 25% of the following
25% of 100 =	25% of 4 =	25% of 8 =
25% of 60 =	25% of 20 =	25% of 20 =
25% of 8 =	25% of 28 =	25% of 48 =
25% of 24 =	25% of 48 =	25% of 80 =
25% of 56 =	25% of 120 =	25% of 64 =
25% of 72 =	25% of 32 =	25% of 96 =
25% of 48 =	25% of 240 =	25% of 100 =
25% of 80 =	25% of 180 =	25% of 200 =
25% of 64 =	25% of 400 =	25% of 300 =
25% of 96 =	25% of 144 =	25% of 180 =
25% of 500 =	25% of 200 =	25% of 72 =
25% of 52 =	25% of 68 =	25% of 172 =
25% of 88 =	25% of 76 =	25% of 272 =
25% of 188 =	25% of 176 =	25% of 372 =
25% of 288 =	25% of 276 =	25% of 12 =
25% of 48 =	25% of 48 =	25% of 212 =
25% of 248 =	25% of 248 =	25% of 500 =
25% of 400 =	25% of 300 =	25% of 600 =
25% of 800 =	25% of 600 =	25% of 700 =
25% of 700 =	25% of 900 =	25% of 800 =

Maths Minute 24

Andrew Brodie Publications
© A & C Black Publishers Ltd.

Maths Minute 24

Andrew Brodie Publications
© A & C Black Publishers Ltd.

Maths Minute 24

Andrew Brodie Publications
© A & C Black Publishers Ltd.

Calculate 25% of the following

25% of 100 = 25

25% of 60 = 15

25% of   8 =   2

25% of 24 =   6

25% of 56 = 14

25% of 72 = 18

25% of 48 = 12

25% of 80 = 20

25% of 64 = 16

25% of 96 = 24

25% of 500 = 125

25% of 52 = 13

25% of 88 = 22

25% of 188 = 47

25% of 288 = 72

25% of 48 = 12

25% of 248 = 62

25% of 400 = 100

25% of 800 = 200

25% of 700 = 175

ANSWERS

Maths Minute 24

Calculate 25% of the following

25% of   4 =   1

25% of 20 =   5

25% of 28 =   7

25% of 48 = 12

25% of 120 = 30

25% of 32 =   8

25% of 240 = 60

25% of 180 = 45

25% of 400 = 100

25% of 144 = 36

25% of 200 = 50

25% of 68 = 17

25% of 76 = 19

25% of 176 = 44

25% of 276 = 69

25% of 48 = 12

25% of 248 = 62

25% of 300 = 75

25% of 600 = 150

25% of 900 = 225

ANSWERS

Maths Minute 24

Calculate 25% of the following

25% of   8 =   2

25% of 20 =   5

25% of 48 = 12

25% of 80 = 20

25% of 64 = 16

25% of 96 = 24

25% of 100 = 25

25% of 200 = 50

25% of 300 = 75

25% of 180 = 45

25% of 72 = 18

25% of 172 = 43

25% of 272 = 68

25% of 372 = 93

25% of 12 =   3

25% of 212 = 53

25% of 500 = 125

25% of 600 = 150

25% of 700 = 175

25% of 800 = 200

ANSWERS

Maths Minute 24

Name   ● Name   ▲ Name

Calculate the following fifths	Calculate the following fifths	Calculate the following fifths
$\frac{1}{5}$ of 20 =	$\frac{1}{5}$ of 50 =	$\frac{1}{5}$ of 80 =
$\frac{1}{5}$ of 30 =	$\frac{1}{5}$ of 75 =	$\frac{1}{5}$ of 70 =
$\frac{1}{5}$ of 5 =	$\frac{1}{5}$ of 30 =	$\frac{1}{5}$ of 15 =
$\frac{1}{5}$ of 25 =	$\frac{1}{5}$ of 10 =	$\frac{1}{5}$ of 20 =
$\frac{1}{5}$ of 15 =	$\frac{1}{5}$ of 40 =	$\frac{1}{5}$ of 30 =
$\frac{1}{5}$ of 50 =	$\frac{1}{5}$ of 25 =	$\frac{1}{5}$ of 35 =
$\frac{1}{5}$ of 95 =	$\frac{1}{5}$ of 65 =	$\frac{1}{5}$ of 100 =
$\frac{1}{5}$ of 60 =	$\frac{1}{5}$ of 55 =	$\frac{1}{5}$ of 45 =
$\frac{1}{5}$ of 85 =	$\frac{1}{5}$ of 20 =	$\frac{1}{5}$ of 65 =
$\frac{1}{5}$ of 75 =	$\frac{1}{5}$ of 60 =	$\frac{1}{5}$ of 85 =
$\frac{2}{5}$ of 10 =	$\frac{2}{5}$ of 40 =	$\frac{2}{5}$ of 5 =
$\frac{2}{5}$ of 30 =	$\frac{2}{5}$ of 50 =	$\frac{2}{5}$ of 20 =
$\frac{2}{5}$ of 15 =	$\frac{2}{5}$ of 10 =	$\frac{2}{5}$ of 35 =
$\frac{2}{5}$ of 60 =	$\frac{2}{5}$ of 55 =	$\frac{2}{5}$ of 45 =
$\frac{2}{5}$ of 20 =	$\frac{2}{5}$ of 30 =	$\frac{2}{5}$ of 40 =
$\frac{3}{5}$ of 20 =	$\frac{3}{5}$ of 30 =	$\frac{3}{5}$ of 40 =
$\frac{3}{5}$ of 15 =	$\frac{3}{5}$ of 35 =	$\frac{3}{5}$ of 30 =
$\frac{3}{5}$ of 25 =	$\frac{3}{5}$ of 15 =	$\frac{3}{5}$ of 10 =
$\frac{4}{5}$ of 45 =	$\frac{4}{5}$ of 45 =	$\frac{4}{5}$ of 50 =
$\frac{4}{5}$ of 60 =	$\frac{4}{5}$ of 70 =	$\frac{4}{5}$ of 80 =

Andrew Brodie Publications
© A & C Black Publishers Ltd.

Andrew Brodie Publications
© A & C Black Publishers Ltd.

Andrew Brodie Publications
© A & C Black Publishers Ltd.

◆ ANSWERS

Calculate the following fifths

$\frac{1}{5}$ of 20 = 4

$\frac{1}{5}$ of 30 = 6

$\frac{1}{5}$ of 5 = 1

$\frac{1}{5}$ of 25 = 5

$\frac{1}{5}$ of 15 = 3

$\frac{1}{5}$ of 50 = 10

$\frac{1}{5}$ of 95 = 19

$\frac{1}{5}$ of 60 = 12

$\frac{1}{5}$ of 85 = 17

$\frac{1}{5}$ of 75 = 15

$\frac{2}{5}$ of 10 = 4

$\frac{2}{5}$ of 30 = 12

$\frac{2}{5}$ of 15 = 6

$\frac{2}{5}$ of 60 = 24

$\frac{2}{5}$ of 20 = 8

$\frac{3}{5}$ of 20 = 12

$\frac{3}{5}$ of 15 = 9

$\frac{3}{5}$ of 25 = 15

$\frac{4}{5}$ of 45 = 36

$\frac{4}{5}$ of 60 = 48

ANSWERS
Maths Minute 25
Andrew Brodie Publications
© A & C Black Publishers Ltd.

● ANSWERS

Calculate the following fifths

$\frac{1}{5}$ of 50 = 10

$\frac{1}{5}$ of 75 = 15

$\frac{1}{5}$ of 30 = 6

$\frac{1}{5}$ of 10 = 2

$\frac{1}{5}$ of 40 = 8

$\frac{1}{5}$ of 25 = 5

$\frac{1}{5}$ of 65 = 13

$\frac{1}{5}$ of 55 = 11

$\frac{1}{5}$ of 20 = 4

$\frac{1}{5}$ of 60 = 12

$\frac{2}{5}$ of 40 = 16

$\frac{2}{5}$ of 50 = 20

$\frac{2}{5}$ of 10 = 4

$\frac{2}{5}$ of 55 = 22

$\frac{2}{5}$ of 30 = 12

$\frac{3}{5}$ of 30 = 18

$\frac{3}{5}$ of 35 = 21

$\frac{3}{5}$ of 15 = 9

$\frac{4}{5}$ of 45 = 36

$\frac{4}{5}$ of 70 = 56

ANSWERS
Maths Minute 25
Andrew Brodie Publications
© A & C Black Publishers Ltd.

▲ ANSWERS

Calculate the following fifths

$\frac{1}{5}$ of 80 = 16

$\frac{1}{5}$ of 70 = 14

$\frac{1}{5}$ of 15 = 3

$\frac{1}{5}$ of 20 = 4

$\frac{1}{5}$ of 30 = 6

$\frac{1}{5}$ of 35 = 7

$\frac{1}{5}$ of 100 = 20

$\frac{1}{5}$ of 45 = 9

$\frac{1}{5}$ of 65 = 13

$\frac{1}{5}$ of 85 = 17

$\frac{2}{5}$ of 5 = 2

$\frac{2}{5}$ of 20 = 8

$\frac{2}{5}$ of 35 = 14

$\frac{2}{5}$ of 45 = 18

$\frac{2}{5}$ of 40 = 16

$\frac{3}{5}$ of 40 = 24

$\frac{3}{5}$ of 30 = 18

$\frac{3}{5}$ of 10 = 6

$\frac{4}{5}$ of 50 = 40

$\frac{4}{5}$ of 80 = 64

ANSWERS
Maths Minute 25
Andrew Brodie Publications
© A & C Black Publishers Ltd.

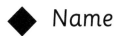 Name    Name   ▲ Name

Multiplication with 1 decimal place	Multiplication with 1 decimal place	Multiplication with 1 decimal place
2 x 0·6 =	1 x 0·5 =	9 x 0·3 =
9 x 0·4 =	2 x 0·6 =	2 x 0·6 =
8 x 0·3 =	6 x 0·3 =	9 x 0·9 =
10 x 0·8 =	8 x 0·4 =	6 x 0·4 =
8 x 0·2 =	7 x 0·2 =	1 x 0·7 =
7 x 0·1 =	10 x 0·8 =	5 x 0·8 =
6 x 0·9 =	9 x 0·6 =	4 x 0·2 =
10 x 0·6 =	2 x 0·1 =	8 x 0·1 =
7 x 0·6 =	4 x 0·7 =	7 x 0·6 =
5 x 0·3 =	5 x 0·7 =	3 x 0·2 =
3 x 0·2 =	7 x 0·6 =	10 x 0·5 =
2 x 0·5 =	3 x 0·9 =	4 x 0·4 =
1 x 0·7 =	8 x 0·8 =	4 x 0·5 =
9 x 0·9 =	4 x 0·3 =	5 x 0·8 =
5 x 0·8 =	9 x 0·2 =	5 x 0·9 =
4 x 0·6 =	3 x 0·4 =	3 x 0·7 =
6 x 0·5 =	4 x 0·5 =	6 x 0·5 =
7 x 0·3 =	2 x 0·7 =	2 x 0·3 =
3 x 0·6 =	10 x 0·1 =	7 x 0·2 =
4 x 0·8 =	5 x 0·9 =	7 x 0·4 =

Maths Minute 26   **Maths Minute 26**   **Maths Minute 26**

Andrew Brodie Publications
© A & C Black Publishers Ltd.   Andrew Brodie Publications
© A & C Black Publishers Ltd.   Andrew Brodie Publications
© A & C Black Publishers Ltd.

ANSWERS

Multiplication with 1 decimal place

2 x 0·6 = 1·2

9 x 0·4 = 3·6

8 x 0·3 = 2·4

10 x 0·8 = 8

8 x 0·2 = 1·6

7 x 0·1 = 0·7

6 x 0·9 = 5·4

10 x 0·6 = 6

7 x 0·6 = 4·2

5 x 0·3 = 1·5

3 x 0·2 = 0·6

2 x 0·5 = 1

1 x 0·7 = 0·7

9 x 0·9 = 8·1

5 x 0·8 = 4

4 x 0·6 = 2·4

6 x 0·5 = 3

7 x 0·3 = 2·1

3 x 0·6 = 1·8

4 x 0·8 = 3·2

ANSWERS

Multiplication with 1 decimal place

1 x 0.5 = 0.5

2 x 0.6 = 1·2

6 x 0.3 = 1·8

8 x 0.4 = 3·2

7 x 0.2 = 1·4

10 x 0.8 = 8

9 x 0.6 = 5·4

2 x 0.1 = 0·2

4 x 0.7 = 2·8

5 x 0.7 = 3·5

7 x 0.6 = 4·2

3 x 0.9 = 2·7

8 x 0.8 = 6·4

4 x 0.3 = 1·2

9 x 0.2 = 1·8

3 x 0.4 = 1·2

4 x 0.5 = 2

2 x 0.7 = 1·4

10 x 0.1 = 1

5 x 0.9 = 4·5

ANSWERS

Multiplication with 1 decimal place

9 x 0·3 = 2·7

2 x 0·6 = 1·2

9 x 0·9 = 8·1

6 x 0·4 = 2·4

1 x 0·7 = 0·7

5 x 0·8 = 4

4 x 0·2 = 0·8

8 x 0·1 = 0·8

7 x 0·6 = 4·2

3 x 0·2 = 0·6

10 x 0·5 = 5

4 x 0·4 = 1·6

4 x 0·5 = 2

5 x 0·8 = 4

5 x 0·9 = 4·5

3 x 0·7 = 2·1

6 x 0·5 = 3

2 x 0·3 = 0·6

7 x 0·2 = 1·4

7 x 0·4 = 2·8

ANSWERS

Maths Minute 26

Andrew Brodie Publications
© A & C Black Publishers Ltd.

ANSWERS

Maths Minute 26

Andrew Brodie Publications
© A & C Black Publishers Ltd.

ANSWERS

Maths Minute 26

Andrew Brodie Publications
© A & C Black Publishers Ltd.

◆ Name	● Name	▲ Name	✳ Name
How many halves in the following numbers?	How many halves in the following numbers?	How many halves in the following numbers?	How many halves in the following numbers?
$1\frac{1}{2}$ ➡	$2\frac{1}{2}$ ➡	3 ➡	$1\frac{1}{2}$ ➡
$3\frac{1}{2}$ ➡	$4\frac{1}{2}$ ➡	$12\frac{1}{2}$ ➡	2 ➡
4 ➡	1 ➡	15 ➡	$16\frac{1}{2}$ ➡
8 ➡	16 ➡	$2\frac{1}{2}$ ➡	17 ➡
$8\frac{1}{2}$ ➡	$17\frac{1}{2}$ ➡	$10\frac{1}{2}$ ➡	$3\frac{1}{2}$ ➡
$7\frac{1}{2}$ ➡	$3\frac{1}{2}$ ➡	$1\frac{1}{2}$ ➡	$11\frac{1}{2}$ ➡
16 ➡	$8\frac{1}{2}$ ➡	$16\frac{1}{2}$ ➡	$15\frac{1}{2}$ ➡
$17\frac{1}{2}$ ➡	$5\frac{1}{2}$ ➡	$4\frac{1}{2}$ ➡	$4\frac{1}{2}$ ➡
$19\frac{1}{2}$ ➡	$19\frac{1}{2}$ ➡	$9\frac{1}{2}$ ➡	$18\frac{1}{2}$ ➡
$20\frac{1}{2}$ ➡	20 ➡	$7\frac{1}{2}$ ➡	$12\frac{1}{2}$ ➡
$36\frac{1}{2}$ ➡	$23\frac{1}{2}$ ➡	36 ➡	$13\frac{1}{2}$ ➡
$82\frac{1}{2}$ ➡	$67\frac{1}{2}$ ➡	$54\frac{1}{2}$ ➡	$41\frac{1}{2}$ ➡
$94\frac{1}{2}$ ➡	$30\frac{1}{2}$ ➡	$37\frac{1}{2}$ ➡	$62\frac{1}{2}$ ➡
$77\frac{1}{2}$ ➡	$27\frac{1}{2}$ ➡	$49\frac{1}{2}$ ➡	$33\frac{1}{2}$ ➡
$65\frac{1}{2}$ ➡	$53\frac{1}{2}$ ➡	50 ➡	$71\frac{1}{2}$ ➡
93 ➡	$33\frac{1}{2}$ ➡	$62\frac{1}{2}$ ➡	$82\frac{1}{2}$ ➡
$55\frac{1}{2}$ ➡	29 ➡	$24\frac{1}{2}$ ➡	$90\frac{1}{2}$ ➡
$48\frac{1}{2}$ ➡	$82\frac{1}{2}$ ➡	$77\frac{1}{2}$ ➡	$55\frac{1}{2}$ ➡
$62\frac{1}{2}$ ➡	42 ➡	$81\frac{1}{2}$ ➡	64 ➡
81 ➡	$37\frac{1}{2}$ ➡	100 ➡	$78\frac{1}{2}$ ➡

Maths Minute 27

Andrew Brodie Publications
© A & C Black Publishers Ltd.

◆ ANSWERS

How many halves in the following numbers?

$1\frac{1}{2}$	➡	3
$3\frac{1}{2}$	➡	7
4	➡	8
8	➡	16
$8\frac{1}{2}$	➡	17
$7\frac{1}{2}$	➡	15
16	➡	32
$17\frac{1}{2}$	➡	35
$19\frac{1}{2}$	➡	39
$20\frac{1}{2}$	➡	41
$36\frac{1}{2}$	➡	73
$82\frac{1}{2}$	➡	165
$94\frac{1}{2}$	➡	189
$77\frac{1}{2}$	➡	155
$65\frac{1}{2}$	➡	131
93	➡	186
$55\frac{1}{2}$	➡	111
$48\frac{1}{2}$	➡	97
$62\frac{1}{2}$	➡	125
81	➡	162

● ANSWERS

How many halves in the following numbers?

$2\frac{1}{2}$	➡	5
$4\frac{1}{2}$	➡	9
1	➡	2
16	➡	32
$17\frac{1}{2}$	➡	35
$3\frac{1}{2}$	➡	7
$8\frac{1}{2}$	➡	17
$5\frac{1}{2}$	➡	11
$19\frac{1}{2}$	➡	39
20	➡	40
$23\frac{1}{2}$	➡	47
$67\frac{1}{2}$	➡	135
$30\frac{1}{2}$	➡	61
$27\frac{1}{2}$	➡	55
$53\frac{1}{2}$	➡	107
$33\frac{1}{2}$	➡	67
29	➡	58
$82\frac{1}{2}$	➡	165
42	➡	84
$37\frac{1}{2}$	➡	75

▲ ANSWERS

How many halves in the following numbers?

3	➡	6
$12\frac{1}{2}$	➡	25
15	➡	30
$2\frac{1}{2}$	➡	5
$10\frac{1}{2}$	➡	21
$1\frac{1}{2}$	➡	3
$16\frac{1}{2}$	➡	33
$4\frac{1}{2}$	➡	9
$9\frac{1}{2}$	➡	19
$7\frac{1}{2}$	➡	15
36	➡	72
$54\frac{1}{2}$	➡	109
$37\frac{1}{2}$	➡	75
$49\frac{1}{2}$	➡	99
50	➡	100
$62\frac{1}{2}$	➡	125
$24\frac{1}{2}$	➡	49
$77\frac{1}{2}$	➡	155
$81\frac{1}{2}$	➡	163
100	➡	200

✶ ANSWERS

How many halves in the following numbers?

$1\frac{1}{2}$	➡	3
2	➡	4
$16\frac{1}{2}$	➡	33
17	➡	34
$3\frac{1}{2}$	➡	7
$11\frac{1}{2}$	➡	23
$15\frac{1}{2}$	➡	31
$4\frac{1}{2}$	➡	9
$18\frac{1}{2}$	➡	37
$12\frac{1}{2}$	➡	25
$13\frac{1}{2}$	➡	27
$41\frac{1}{2}$	➡	83
$62\frac{1}{2}$	➡	125
$33\frac{1}{2}$	➡	67
$71\frac{1}{2}$	➡	143
$82\frac{1}{2}$	➡	165
$90\frac{1}{2}$	➡	181
$55\frac{1}{2}$	➡	111
64	➡	128
$78\frac{1}{2}$	➡	157

ANSWERS
Maths Minute 27
Andrew Brodie Publications
© A & C Black Publishers Ltd.

ANSWERS
Maths Minute 27
Andrew Brodie Publications
© A & C Black Publishers Ltd.

ANSWERS
Maths Minute 27
Andrew Brodie Publications
© A & C Black Publishers Ltd.

ANSWERS
Maths Minute 27
Andrew Brodie Publications
© A & C Black Publishers Ltd.

◆ Name _____

How many quarters in the following numbers?

$1\frac{1}{4}$ ➡

$2\frac{1}{2}$ ➡

$3\frac{1}{4}$ ➡

$2\frac{3}{4}$ ➡

$2\frac{1}{4}$ ➡

$3\frac{1}{2}$ ➡

4 ➡

$1\frac{1}{2}$ ➡

$5\frac{1}{4}$ ➡

$3\frac{3}{4}$ ➡

$6\frac{1}{4}$ ➡

$9\frac{1}{4}$ ➡

$6\frac{1}{2}$ ➡

$7\frac{1}{4}$ ➡

$9\frac{1}{2}$ ➡

10 ➡

$8\frac{1}{4}$ ➡

$10\frac{1}{2}$ ➡

$6\frac{3}{4}$ ➡

$7\frac{3}{4}$ ➡

Maths Minute 28

Andrew Brodie Publications

● Name _____

How many quarters in the following numbers?

1 ➡

$1\frac{1}{4}$ ➡

2 ➡

$2\frac{1}{4}$ ➡

$2\frac{1}{2}$ ➡

$4\frac{1}{4}$ ➡

$4\frac{3}{4}$ ➡

5 ➡

$5\frac{1}{4}$ ➡

$5\frac{1}{2}$ ➡

$8\frac{1}{4}$ ➡

$8\frac{3}{4}$ ➡

$6\frac{1}{2}$ ➡

$10\frac{1}{4}$ ➡

$7\frac{3}{4}$ ➡

$6\frac{1}{4}$ ➡

$6\frac{3}{4}$ ➡

$9\frac{3}{4}$ ➡

$9\frac{1}{4}$ ➡

$7\frac{1}{2}$ ➡

Maths Minute 28

Andrew Brodie Publications

▲ Name _____

How many quarters in the following numbers?

$\frac{1}{2}$ ➡

$2\frac{1}{4}$ ➡

$3\frac{1}{4}$ ➡

$4\frac{1}{4}$ ➡

$2\frac{1}{2}$ ➡

$1\frac{1}{2}$ ➡

5 ➡

$4\frac{1}{2}$ ➡

$4\frac{3}{4}$ ➡

$5\frac{1}{4}$ ➡

$6\frac{1}{4}$ ➡

$6\frac{1}{2}$ ➡

$6\frac{3}{4}$ ➡

8 ➡

$8\frac{1}{2}$ ➡

$9\frac{1}{4}$ ➡

$7\frac{1}{2}$ ➡

$9\frac{1}{2}$ ➡

$10\frac{3}{4}$ ➡

$10\frac{1}{2}$ ➡

Maths Minute 28

Andrew Brodie Publications

✳ Name _____

How many quarters in the following numbers?

$1\frac{1}{2}$ ➡

$1\frac{3}{4}$ ➡

$2\frac{1}{2}$ ➡

$4\frac{1}{4}$ ➡

$5\frac{1}{4}$ ➡

$3\frac{1}{2}$ ➡

$3\frac{1}{4}$ ➡

$3\frac{3}{4}$ ➡

4 ➡

$2\frac{3}{4}$ ➡

$8\frac{1}{4}$ ➡

$8\frac{1}{2}$ ➡

$9\frac{1}{4}$ ➡

$10\frac{1}{4}$ ➡

$6\frac{3}{4}$ ➡

$7\frac{1}{4}$ ➡

$9\frac{3}{4}$ ➡

$6\frac{1}{4}$ ➡

$7\frac{1}{2}$ ➡

10 ➡

Maths Minute 28

Andrew Brodie Publications

 **ANSWERS**

How many quarters in the following numbers?

$1\frac{1}{4}$	➡	5
$2\frac{1}{2}$	➡	10
$3\frac{1}{4}$	➡	13
$2\frac{3}{4}$	➡	11
$2\frac{1}{4}$	➡	9
$3\frac{1}{2}$	➡	14
4	➡	16
$1\frac{1}{2}$	➡	6
$5\frac{1}{4}$	➡	21
$3\frac{3}{4}$	➡	15
$6\frac{1}{4}$	➡	25
$9\frac{1}{4}$	➡	37
$6\frac{1}{2}$	➡	26
$7\frac{1}{4}$	➡	29
$9\frac{1}{2}$	➡	38
10	➡	40
$8\frac{1}{4}$	➡	33
$10\frac{1}{2}$	➡	42
$6\frac{3}{4}$	➡	27
$7\frac{3}{4}$	➡	31

 **ANSWERS**

How many quarters in the following numbers?

1	➡	4
$1\frac{1}{4}$	➡	5
2	➡	8
$2\frac{1}{4}$	➡	9
$2\frac{1}{2}$	➡	10
$4\frac{1}{4}$	➡	17
$4\frac{3}{4}$	➡	19
5	➡	20
$5\frac{1}{4}$	➡	21
$5\frac{1}{2}$	➡	22
$8\frac{1}{4}$	➡	33
$8\frac{3}{4}$	➡	35
$6\frac{1}{2}$	➡	25
$10\frac{1}{4}$	➡	41
$7\frac{3}{4}$	➡	31
$6\frac{1}{4}$	➡	25
$6\frac{3}{4}$	➡	27
$9\frac{3}{4}$	➡	39
$9\frac{1}{4}$	➡	37
$7\frac{1}{2}$	➡	30

▲ **ANSWERS**

How many quarters in the following numbers?

$\frac{1}{2}$	➡	2
$2\frac{1}{4}$	➡	9
$3\frac{1}{4}$	➡	13
$4\frac{1}{4}$	➡	17
$2\frac{1}{2}$	➡	10
$1\frac{1}{2}$	➡	6
5	➡	20
$4\frac{1}{2}$	➡	18
$4\frac{3}{4}$	➡	19
$5\frac{1}{4}$	➡	21
$6\frac{1}{4}$	➡	25
$6\frac{1}{2}$	➡	26
$6\frac{3}{4}$	➡	27
8	➡	32
$8\frac{1}{2}$	➡	34
$9\frac{1}{4}$	➡	37
$7\frac{1}{2}$	➡	30
$9\frac{1}{2}$	➡	38
$10\frac{3}{4}$	➡	43
$10\frac{1}{2}$	➡	42

 **ANSWERS**

How many quarters in the following numbers?

$1\frac{1}{2}$	➡	6
$1\frac{3}{4}$	➡	7
$2\frac{1}{2}$	➡	10
$4\frac{1}{4}$	➡	17
$5\frac{1}{4}$	➡	21
$3\frac{1}{2}$	➡	14
$3\frac{1}{4}$	➡	13
$3\frac{3}{4}$	➡	15
4	➡	16
$2\frac{3}{4}$	➡	11
$8\frac{1}{4}$	➡	33
$8\frac{1}{2}$	➡	34
$9\frac{1}{4}$	➡	37
$10\frac{1}{4}$	➡	41
$6\frac{3}{4}$	➡	27
$7\frac{1}{4}$	➡	29
$9\frac{3}{4}$	➡	39
$6\frac{1}{4}$	➡	25
$7\frac{1}{2}$	➡	30
10	➡	40

ANSWERS

Maths Minute 28

Andrew Brodie Publications
© A & C Black Publishers Ltd.

ANSWERS

Maths Minute 28

Andrew Brodie Publications
© A & C Black Publishers Ltd.

ANSWERS

Maths Minute 28

Andrew Brodie Publications
© A & C Black Publishers Ltd.

ANSWERS

Maths Minute 28

Andrew Brodie Publications
© A & C Black Publishers Ltd.

◆ Name	● Name	▲ Name	✳ Name
3 digit add 2 digit numbers	3 digit add 2 digit numbers	3 digit add 2 digit numbers	3 digit add 2 digit numbers
$230 + 16 =$	$206 + 10 =$	$214 + 20 =$	$272 + 15 =$
$421 + 14 =$	$756 + 12 =$	$609 + 72 =$	$505 + 25 =$
$544 + 20 =$	$337 + 13 =$	$142 + 11 =$	$378 + 30 =$
$200 + 69 =$	$537 + 31 =$	$579 + 21 =$	$501 + 89 =$
$910 + 27 =$	$162 + 21 =$	$472 + 16 =$	$137 + 41 =$
$111 + 36 =$	$273 + 27 =$	$620 + 15 =$	$911 + 26 =$
$172 + 19 =$	$555 + 30 =$	$480 + 20 =$	$411 + 82 =$
$817 + 20 =$	$728 + 42 =$	$906 + 70 =$	$281 + 11 =$
$926 + 13 =$	$488 + 12 =$	$272 + 13 =$	$224 + 56 =$
$316 + 13 =$	$618 + 22 =$	$652 + 48 =$	$624 + 16 =$
$440 + 39 =$	$828 + 32 =$	$139 + 21 =$	$184 + 16 =$
$540 + 29 =$	$129 + 41 =$	$898 + 36 =$	$954 + 16 =$
$670 + 71 =$	$139 + 41 =$	$354 + 52 =$	$594 + 16 =$
$462 + 17 =$	$149 + 41 =$	$367 + 23 =$	$594 + 26 =$
$470 + 17 =$	$159 + 41 =$	$823 + 17 =$	$594 + 36 =$
$526 + 90 =$	$428 + 72 =$	$633 + 17 =$	$594 + 46 =$
$536 + 90 =$	$138 + 62 =$	$543 + 17 =$	$156 + 11 =$
$546 + 90 =$	$842 + 48 =$	$443 + 27 =$	$728 + 10 =$
$556 + 90 =$	$203 + 53 =$	$207 + 33 =$	$336 + 60 =$
$627 + 31 =$	$512 + 62 =$	$737 + 33 =$	$610 + 56 =$

Andrew Brodie Publications | Andrew Brodie Publications | Andrew Brodie Publications | Andrew Brodie Publications

♦ **ANSWERS**

3 digit add 2 digit
numbers

230 + 16 = 246

421 + 14 = 435

544 + 20 = 564

200 + 69 = 269

910 + 27 = 937

111 + 36 = 147

172 + 19 = 191

817 + 20 = 837

926 + 13 = 939

316 + 13 = 329

440 + 39 = 479

540 + 29 = 569

670 + 71 = 741

462 + 17 = 479

470 + 17 = 487

526 + 90 = 616

536 + 90 = 626

546 + 90 = 636

556 + 90 = 646

627 + 31 = 658

ANSWERS

Maths Minute 29

Andrew Brodie Publications
© A & C Black Publishers Ltd.

● **ANSWERS**

3 digit add 2 digit
numbers

206 + 10 = 216

756 + 12 = 768

337 + 13 = 350

537 + 31 = 568

162 + 21 = 183

273 + 27 = 300

555 + 30 = 585

728 + 42 = 770

488 + 12 = 500

618 + 22 = 640

828 + 32 = 860

129 + 41 = 170

139 + 41 = 180

149 + 41 = 190

159 + 41 = 200

428 + 72 = 500

138 + 62 = 200

842 + 48 = 890

203 + 53 = 256

512 + 62 = 574

ANSWERS

Maths Minute 29

Andrew Brodie Publications
© A & C Black Publishers Ltd.

▲ **ANSWERS**

3 digit add 2 digit
numbers

214 + 20 = 234

609 + 72 = 681

142 + 11 = 153

579 + 21 = 600

472 + 16 = 488

620 + 15 = 635

480 + 20 = 500

906 + 70 = 976

272 + 13 = 285

652 + 48 = 700

139 + 21 = 160

898 + 36 = 934

354 + 52 = 406

367 + 23 = 390

823 + 17 = 840

633 + 17 = 650

543 + 17 = 560

443 + 27 = 470

207 + 33 = 240

737 + 33 = 770

ANSWERS

Maths Minute 29

Andrew Brodie Publications
© A & C Black Publishers Ltd.

✴ **ANSWERS**

3 digit add 2 digit
numbers

272 + 15 = 287

505 + 25 = 530

378 + 30 = 408

501 + 89 = 590

137 + 41 = 178

911 + 26 = 937

411 + 82 = 493

281 + 11 = 292

224 + 56 = 280

624 + 16 = 640

184 + 16 = 200

954 + 16 = 970

594 + 16 = 610

594 + 26 = 620

594 + 36 = 630

594 + 46 = 640

156 + 11 = 167

728 + 10 = 738

336 + 60 = 396

610 + 56 = 666

ANSWERS

Maths Minute 29

Andrew Brodie Publications
© A & C Black Publishers Ltd.

◆ Name	● Name	▲ Name	✸ Name
Addition with 1 decimal place	**Addition with 1 decimal place**	**Addition with 1 decimal place**	**Addition with 1 decimal place**
$1·6 + 4·2 =$	$2·4 + 3·2 =$	$3·9 + 1·0 =$	$3·5 + 1·4 =$
$4·8 + 5·1 =$	$5·5 + 1·4 =$	$4·1 + 3·6 =$	$4·1 + 3·4 =$
$5·5 + 4·4 =$	$4·6 + 2·3 =$	$1·4 + 2·4 =$	$0·1 + 6·2 =$
$3·6 + 2·3 =$	$6·1 + 3·8 =$	$3·7 + 5·2 =$	$8·4 + 1·3 =$
$9·2 + 0·6 =$	$1·6 + 6·2 =$	$6·5 + 3·4 =$	$3·6 + 3·3 =$
$4·9 + 4·0 =$	$2·7 + 3·1 =$	$3·3 + 3·5 =$	$7·7 + 2·2 =$
$3·5 + 2·4 =$	$6·7 + 2·1 =$	$6·3 + 3·4 =$	$1·4 + 6·3 =$
$5·6 + 4·3 =$	$4·0 + 5·9 =$	$1·6 + 6·1 =$	$8·6 + 1·3 =$
$2·7 + 1·2 =$	$7·6 + 3·2 =$	$6·1 + 1·6 =$	$4·2 + 5·7 =$
$8·7 + 2·2 =$	$5·1 + 4·8 =$	$4·4 + 2·4 =$	$7·6 + 2·3 =$
$5·0 + 5·6 =$	$9·3 + 2·4 =$	$7·4 + 1·3 =$	$0·7 + 8·4 =$
$1·4 + 8·5 =$	$1·5 + 3·7 =$	$2·8 + 3·1 =$	$9·1 + 0·3 =$
$6·2 + 3·9 =$	$8·4 + 1·6 =$	$7·1 + 4·2 =$	$3·4 + 8·2 =$
$8·3 + 1·8 =$	$2·9 + 3·4 =$	$5·8 + 5·1 =$	$7·1 + 1·9 =$
$2·6 + 1·6 =$	$7·5 + 2·7 =$	$4·7 + 3·8 =$	$4·3 + 8·3 =$
$7·9 + 2·7 =$	$4·8 + 3·3 =$	$8·1 + 4·6 =$	$1·8 + 6·2 =$
$4·1 + 3·8 =$	$7·2 + 5·5 =$	$1·9 + 8·8 =$	$5·5 + 5·5 =$
$7·5 + 3·6 =$	$3·1 + 6·9 =$	$9·2 + 9·3 =$	$6·9 + 6·3 =$
$1·8 + 7·4 =$	$6·6 + 4·4 =$	$5·6 + 6·8 =$	$2·3 + 4·9 =$
$6·3 + 2·9 =$	$5·9 + 2·1 =$	$5·7 + 7·8 =$	$6·5 + 3·5 =$

Maths Minute 30 | **Maths Minute 30** | **Maths Minute 30** | **Maths Minute 30**

Andrew Brodie Publications   Andrew Brodie Publications   Andrew Brodie Publications   Andrew Brodie Publications

◆ **ANSWERS**

Addition with 1
decimal place

● **ANSWERS**

Addition with 1
decimal place

▲ **ANSWERS**

Addition with 1
decimal place

✶ **ANSWERS**

Addition with 1
decimal place

$1.6 + 4.2 = 5.8$	$2.4 + 3.2 = 5.6$	$3.9 + 1.0 = 4.9$	$3.5 + 1.4 = 4.9$
$4.8 + 5.1 = 9.9$	$5.5 + 1.4 = 6.9$	$4.1 + 3.6 = 7.7$	$4.1 + 3.4 = 7.5$
$5.5 + 4.4 = 9.9$	$4.6 + 2.3 = 6.9$	$1.4 + 2.4 = 3.8$	$0.1 + 6.2 = 6.3$
$3.6 + 2.3 = 5.9$	$6.1 + 3.8 = 9.9$	$3.7 + 5.2 = 8.9$	$8.4 + 1.3 = 9.7$
$9.2 + 0.6 = 9.8$	$1.6 + 6.2 = 7.8$	$6.5 + 3.4 = 9.9$	$3.6 + 3.3 = 6.9$
$4.9 + 4.0 = 8.9$	$2.7 + 3.1 = 5.8$	$3.3 + 3.5 = 6.8$	$7.7 + 2.2 = 9.9$
$3.5 + 2.4 = 5.9$	$6.7 + 2.1 = 8.8$	$6.3 + 3.4 = 9.7$	$1.4 + 6.3 = 7.7$
$5.6 + 4.3 = 9.9$	$4.0 + 5.9 = 9.9$	$1.6 + 6.1 = 7.7$	$8.6 + 1.3 = 9.9$
$2.7 + 1.2 = 3.9$	$7.6 + 3.2 = 10.8$	$6.1 + 1.6 = 7.7$	$4.2 + 5.7 = 9.9$
$8.7 + 2.2 = 10.9$	$5.1 + 4.8 = 9.9$	$4.4 + 2.4 = 6.8$	$7.6 + 2.3 = 9.9$
$5.0 + 5.6 = 10.6$	$9.3 + 2.4 = 11.7$	$7.4 + 1.3 = 8.7$	$0.7 + 8.4 = 9.1$
$1.4 + 8.5 = 9.9$	$1.5 + 3.7 = 5.2$	$2.8 + 3.1 = 5.9$	$9.1 + 0.3 = 9.4$
$6.2 + 3.9 = 10.1$	$8.4 + 1.6 = 10$	$7.1 + 4.2 = 11.3$	$3.4 + 8.2 = 11.6$
$8.3 + 1.8 = 10.1$	$2.9 + 3.4 = 6.3$	$5.8 + 5.1 = 10.9$	$7.1 + 1.9 = 9$
$2.6 + 1.6 = 4.2$	$7.5 + 2.7 = 10.2$	$4.7 + 3.8 = 8.5$	$4.3 + 8.3 = 12.6$
$7.9 + 2.7 = 10.6$	$4.8 + 3.3 = 8.1$	$8.1 + 4.6 = 12.7$	$1.8 + 6.2 = 8$
$4.1 + 3.8 = 7.9$	$7.2 + 5.5 = 12.7$	$1.9 + 8.8 = 10.7$	$5.5 + 5.5 = 11$
$7.5 + 3.6 = 11.1$	$3.1 + 6.9 = 10$	$9.2 + 9.3 = 18.5$	$6.9 + 6.3 = 13.2$
$1.8 + 7.4 = 9.2$	$6.6 + 4.4 = 11$	$5.6 + 6.8 = 12.4$	$2.3 + 4.9 = 7.2$
$6.3 + 2.9 = 9.2$	$5.9 + 2.1 = 8$	$5.7 + 7.8 = 13.5$	$6.5 + 3.5 = 10$

ANSWERS

Maths Minute 30

Andrew Brodie Publications
© A & C Black Publishers Ltd.

ANSWERS

Maths Minute 30

Andrew Brodie Publications
© A & C Black Publishers Ltd.

ANSWERS

Maths Minute 30

Andrew Brodie Publications
© A & C Black Publishers Ltd.

ANSWERS

Maths Minute 30

Andrew Brodie Publications
© A & C Black Publishers Ltd.

◆ Name	● Name	▲ Name	✹ Name
3 digit multiples of 10 x 2,3,4,5,6,7,8 & 9	3 digit multiples of 10 x 2,3,4,5,6,7,8 & 9	3 digit multiples of 10 x 2,3,4,5,6,7,8 & 9	3 digit multiples of 10 x 2,3,4,5,6,7,8 & 9
120 x 7 =	200 x 9 =	160 x 7 =	190 x 6 =
150 x 8 =	160 x 8 =	410 x 2 =	470 x 1 =
820 x 1 =	420 x 5 =	400 x 9 =	350 x 2 =
400 x 9 =	890 x 2 =	140 x 8 =	220 x 5 =
740 x 2 =	350 x 4 =	610 x 4 =	610 x 6 =
100 x 9 =	550 x 3 =	220 x 3 =	710 x 4 =
830 x 2 =	100 x 9 =	580 x 1 =	330 x 4 =
700 x 7 =	330 x 8 =	700 x 8 =	490 x 3 =
450 x 2 =	520 x 2 =	350 x 7 =	100 x 7 =
580 x 5 =	210 x 7 =	630 x 2 =	810 x 3 =
900 x 2 =	400 x 4 =	120 x 9 =	500 x 6 =
420 x 4 =	510 x 6 =	740 x 4 =	240 x 5 =
910 x 3 =	110 x 5 =	450 x 6 =	730 x 3 =
560 x 4 =	480 x 1 =	230 x 6 =	310 x 7 =
630 x 3 =	360 x 6 =	530 x 5 =	820 x 2 =
230 x 3 =	730 x 3 =	190 x 6 =	140 x 8 =

Maths Minute 31

Andrew Brodie Publications
© A & C Black Publishers Ltd.

Maths Minute 31

Andrew Brodie Publications
© A & C Black Publishers Ltd.

Maths Minute 31

Andrew Brodie Publications
© A & C Black Publishers Ltd.

Maths Minute 31

Andrew Brodie Publications
© A & C Black Publishers Ltd.

120 x 7 = 840

150 x 8 = 1200

820 x 1 = 820

400 x 9 = 3600

740 x 2 = 1480

100 x 9 = 900

830 x 2 = 1660

700 x 7 = 4900

450 x 2 = 900

580 x 5 = 2900

900 x 2 = 1800

420 x 4 = 1680

910 x 3 = 2730

560 x 4 = 2240

630 x 3 = 1890

230 x 3 = 690

ANSWERS
Maths Minute 31
Andrew Brodie Publications
© A & C Black Publishers Ltd.

---

200 x 9 = 1800

160 x 8 = 1280

420 x 5 = 2100

890 x 2 = 1780

350 x 4 = 1400

550 x 3 = 1650

100 x 9 = 900

330 x 8 = 2640

520 x 2 = 1040

210 x 7 = 1470

400 x 4 = 1600

510 x 6 = 3060

110 x 5 = 550

480 x 1 = 480

360 x 6 = 2160

730 x 3 = 2190

ANSWERS
Maths Minute 31
Andrew Brodie Publications
© A & C Black Publishers Ltd.

---

160 x 7 = 1120

410 x 2 = 820

400 x 9 = 3600

140 x 8 = 1120

610 x 4 = 2440

220 x 3 = 660

580 x 1 = 580

700 x 8 = 5600

350 x 7 = 2450

630 x 2 = 1260

120 x 9 = 1080

740 x 4 = 2960

450 x 6 = 2700

230 x 6 = 1380

530 x 5 = 2650

190 x 6 = 1140

ANSWERS
Maths Minute 31
Andrew Brodie Publications
© A & C Black Publishers Ltd.

---

190 x 6 = 1140

470 x 1 = 470

350 x 2 = 700

220 x 5 = 1100

610 x 6 = 3660

710 x 4 = 2840

330 x 4 = 1320

490 x 3 = 1470

100 x 7 = 700

810 x 3 = 2430

500 x 6 = 3000

240 x 5 = 1200

730 x 3 = 2190

310 x 7 = 2170

820 x 2 = 1640

140 x 8 = 1120

ANSWERS
Maths Minute 31
Andrew Brodie Publications
© A & C Black Publishers Ltd.

◆ Name	● Name	▲ Name	✳ Name
3 digit minus 2 digit numbers	3 digit minus 2 digit numbers	3 digit minus 2 digit numbers	3 digit minus 2 digit numbers
$672 - 11 =$	$398 - 72 =$	$497 - 54 =$	$598 - 56 =$
$786 - 24 =$	$468 - 33 =$	$698 - 62 =$	$476 - 23 =$
$964 - 32 =$	$375 - 44 =$	$285 - 83 =$	$819 - 19 =$
$875 - 51 =$	$369 - 27 =$	$565 - 42 =$	$762 - 41 =$
$998 - 44 =$	$958 - 35 =$	$486 - 75 =$	$847 - 36 =$
$875 - 33 =$	$636 - 16 =$	$791 - 80 =$	$915 - 12 =$
$688 - 46 =$	$795 - 84 =$	$349 - 32 =$	$487 - 64 =$
$674 - 31 =$	$483 - 72 =$	$826 - 17 =$	$675 - 53 =$
$984 - 43 =$	$974 - 62 =$	$784 - 62 =$	$893 - 72 =$
$598 - 87 =$	$829 - 17 =$	$138 - 18 =$	$972 - 41 =$
$477 - 66 =$	$999 - 88 =$	$496 - 83 =$	$846 - 25 =$
$389 - 45 =$	$349 - 26 =$	$277 - 65 =$	$627 - 15 =$
$298 - 67 =$	$297 - 35 =$	$489 - 46 =$	$397 - 85 =$
$378 - 22 =$	$488 - 47 =$	$598 - 58 =$	$565 - 53 =$
$681 - 81 =$	$698 - 86 =$	$381 - 70 =$	$429 - 17 =$
$536 - 28 =$	$933 - 36 =$	$241 - 34 =$	$227 - 17 =$

Maths Minute 32

Andrew Brodie Publications
© A & C Black Publishers Ltd.

Maths Minute 32

Andrew Brodie Publications
© A & C Black Publishers Ltd.

Maths Minute 32

Andrew Brodie Publications
© A & C Black Publishers Ltd.

Maths Minute 32

Andrew Brodie Publications
© A & C Black Publishers Ltd.

◆ ANSWERS
3 digit minus 2 digit numbers

$672 - 11 = 661$

$786 - 24 = 762$

$964 - 32 = 932$

$875 - 51 = 824$

$998 - 44 = 954$

$875 - 33 = 842$

$688 - 46 = 642$

$674 - 31 = 643$

$984 - 43 = 941$

$598 - 87 = 511$

$477 - 66 = 411$

$389 - 45 = 344$

$298 - 67 = 231$

$378 - 22 = 356$

$681 - 81 = 600$

$536 - 28 = 508$

● ANSWERS
3 digit minus 2 digit numbers

$398 - 72 = 326$

$468 - 33 = 435$

$375 - 44 = 331$

$369 - 27 = 342$

$958 - 35 = 923$

$636 - 16 = 620$

$795 - 84 = 711$

$483 - 72 = 411$

$974 - 62 = 912$

$829 - 17 = 812$

$999 - 88 = 911$

$349 - 26 = 323$

$297 - 35 = 262$

$488 - 47 = 441$

$698 - 86 = 612$

$933 - 36 = 897$

▲ ANSWERS
3 digit minus 2 digit numbers

$497 - 54 = 443$

$698 - 62 = 636$

$285 - 83 = 202$

$565 - 42 = 523$

$486 - 75 = 411$

$791 - 80 = 711$

$349 - 32 = 317$

$826 - 17 = 809$

$784 - 62 = 722$

$138 - 18 = 120$

$496 - 83 = 413$

$277 - 65 = 212$

$489 - 46 = 443$

$598 - 58 = 540$

$381 - 70 = 311$

$241 - 34 = 207$

✹ ANSWERS
3 digit minus 2 digit numbers

$598 - 56 = 542$

$476 - 23 = 453$

$819 - 19 = 800$

$762 - 41 = 721$

$847 - 36 = 811$

$915 - 12 = 903$

$487 - 64 = 423$

$675 - 53 = 622$

$893 - 72 = 821$

$972 - 41 = 931$

$846 - 25 = 821$

$627 - 15 = 612$

$397 - 85 = 312$

$565 - 53 = 512$

$429 - 17 = 412$

$227 - 17 = 210$

ANSWERS
Maths Minute 32

Andrew Brodie Publications
© A & C Black Publishers Ltd.

ANSWERS
Maths Minute 32

Andrew Brodie Publications
© A & C Black Publishers Ltd.

ANSWERS
Maths Minute 32

Andrew Brodie Publications
© A & C Black Publishers Ltd.

ANSWERS
Maths Minute 32

Andrew Brodie Publications
© A & C Black Publishers Ltd.

◆ Name	● Name	▲ Name
3 digit add 3 digit numbers	3 digit add 3 digit numbers	3 digit add 3 digit numbers
295 + 300 =	262 + 326 =	123 + 444 =
279 + 120 =	433 + 142 =	270 + 319 =
369 + 130 =	501 + 398 =	639 + 140 =
456 + 120 =	124 + 561 =	742 + 147 =
592 + 301 =	600 + 189 =	752 + 206 =
787 + 202 =	739 + 120 =	300 + 674 =
610 + 379 =	749 + 120 =	569 + 230 =
432 + 164 =	351 + 238 =	405 + 294 =
815 + 184 =	326 + 621 =	450 + 128 =
741 + 127 =	287 + 712 =	173 + 316 =
444 + 333 =	481 + 318 =	380 + 204 =
563 + 126 =	139 + 720 =	625 + 152 =
622 + 315 =	598 + 201 =	233 + 366 =
156 + 842 =	610 + 359 =	561 + 128 =
156 + 852 =	436 + 148 =	287 + 216 =
514 + 328 =	529 + 327 =	981 + 100 =

Maths Minute 33

Andrew Brodie Publications
© A & C Black Publishers Ltd.

Maths Minute 33

Andrew Brodie Publications
© A & C Black Publishers Ltd.

Maths Minute 33

Andrew Brodie Publications
© A & C Black Publishers Ltd.

◆ ANSWERS
3 digit add 3 digit numbers

$295 + 300 = 595$

$279 + 120 = 399$

$369 + 130 = 499$

$456 + 120 = 576$

$592 + 301 = 893$

$787 + 202 = 989$

$610 + 379 = 989$

$432 + 164 = 596$

$815 + 184 = 999$

$741 + 127 = 868$

$444 + 333 = 777$

$563 + 126 = 689$

$622 + 315 = 937$

$156 + 842 = 998$

$156 + 852 = 1008$

$514 + 328 = 842$

ANSWERS

Maths Minute 33

Andrew Brodie Publications
© A & C Black Publishers Ltd.

● ANSWERS
3 digit add 3 digit numbers

$262 + 326 = 588$

$433 + 142 = 575$

$501 + 398 = 899$

$124 + 561 = 685$

$600 + 189 = 789$

$739 + 120 = 859$

$749 + 120 = 869$

$351 + 238 = 589$

$326 + 621 = 947$

$287 + 712 = 999$

$481 + 318 = 799$

$139 + 720 = 859$

$598 + 201 = 799$

$610 + 359 = 969$

$436 + 148 = 584$

$529 + 327 = 856$

ANSWERS

Maths Minute 33

Andrew Brodie Publications
© A & C Black Publishers Ltd.

▲ ANSWERS
3 digit add 3 digit numbers

$123 + 444 = 567$

$270 + 319 = 589$

$639 + 140 = 779$

$742 + 147 = 889$

$752 + 206 = 958$

$300 + 674 = 974$

$569 + 230 = 799$

$405 + 294 = 699$

$450 + 128 = 578$

$173 + 316 = 489$

$380 + 204 = 584$

$625 + 152 = 777$

$233 + 366 = 599$

$561 + 128 = 689$

$287 + 216 = 503$

$981 + 100 = 1081$

ANSWERS

Maths Minute 33

Andrew Brodie Publications
© A & C Black Publishers Ltd.

◆ Name	● Name	▲ Name	✷ Name
4 digit add 2 digit numbers	4 digit add 2 digit numbers	4 digit add 2 digit numbers	4 digit add 2 digit numbers
3427 + 11 =	3444 + 14 =	2313 + 11 =	2316 + 10 =
1429 + 12 =	6340 + 15 =	3491 + 18 =	8419 + 13 =
8401 + 10 =	1174 + 17 =	6981 + 19 =	3692 + 12 =
3518 + 17 =	7480 + 16 =	5051 + 12 =	9420 + 11 =
5622 + 14 =	3819 + 12 =	7286 + 17 =	4811 + 17 =
4062 + 19 =	8411 + 11 =	5930 + 15 =	6927 + 15 =
8721 + 20 =	5926 + 13 =	1528 + 13 =	5000 + 19 =
1336 + 13 =	1369 + 10 =	7429 + 14 =	1729 + 14 =
7320 + 43 =	7654 + 36 =	3331 + 36 =	9116 + 24 =
3001 + 69 =	5505 + 25 =	2418 + 42 =	3781 + 89 =
9026 + 71 =	2991 + 99 =	8196 + 39 =	5821 + 90 =
6017 + 37 =	8126 + 15 =	4601 + 71 =	6202 + 19 =
1428 + 14 =	6787 + 13 =	9101 + 50 =	2418 + 86 =
5260 + 24 =	1678 + 36 =	1397 + 40 =	6036 + 36 =
5360 + 24 =	9901 + 89 =	9911 + 44 =	1864 + 62 =
4987 + 33 =	2480 + 63 =	5697 + 81 =	8692 + 73 =

Maths Minute 34

Andrew Brodie Publications
© A & C Black Publishers Ltd.

Maths Minute 34

Andrew Brodie Publications
© A & C Black Publishers Ltd.

Maths Minute 34

Andrew Brodie Publications
© A & C Black Publishers Ltd.

Maths Minute 34

Andrew Brodie Publications
© A & C Black Publishers Ltd.

◆ ANSWERS

4 digit add 2 digit numbers

3427 + 11 = 3438

1429 + 12 = 1441

8401 + 10 = 8411

3518 + 17 = 3535

5622 + 14 = 5636

4062 + 19 = 4081

8721 + 20 = 8741

1336 + 13 = 1349

7320 + 43 = 7363

3001 + 69 = 3070

9026 + 71 = 9097

6017 + 37 = 6054

1428 + 14 = 1442

5260 + 24 = 5284

5360 + 24 = 5384

4987 + 33 = 5020

ANSWERS

Maths Minute 34

Andrew Brodie Publications
© A & C Black Publishers Ltd.

● ANSWERS

4 digit add 2 digit numbers

3444 + 14 = 3458

6340 + 15 = 6355

1174 + 17 = 1191

7480 + 16 = 7496

3819 + 12 = 3831

8411 + 11 = 8422

5926 + 13 = 5939

1369 + 10 = 1379

7654 + 36 = 7690

5505 + 25 = 5530

2991 + 99 = 3090

8126 + 15 = 8141

6787 + 13 = 6800

1678 + 36 = 1714

9901 + 89 = 9990

2480 + 63 = 2543

ANSWERS

Maths Minute 34

Andrew Brodie Publications
© A & C Black Publishers Ltd.

▲ ANSWERS

4 digit add 2 digit numbers

2313 + 11 = 2324

3491 + 18 = 3509

6981 + 19 = 7000

5051 + 12 = 5063

7286 + 17 = 7303

5930 + 15 = 5945

1528 + 13 = 1541

7429 + 14 = 7443

3331 + 36 = 3367

2418 + 42 = 2460

8196 + 39 = 8235

4601 + 71 = 4672

9101 + 50 = 9151

1397 + 40 = 1437

9911 + 44 = 9955

5697 + 81 = 5778

ANSWERS

Maths Minute 34

Andrew Brodie Publications
© A & C Black Publishers Ltd.

✹ ANSWERS

4 digit add 2 digit numbers

2316 + 10 = 2326

8419 + 13 = 8432

3692 + 12 = 3704

9420 + 11 = 9431

4811 + 17 = 4828

6927 + 15 = 6942

5000 + 19 = 5019

1729 + 14 = 1743

9116 + 24 = 9140

3781 + 89 = 3870

5821 + 90 = 5911

6202 + 19 = 6221

2418 + 86 = 2504

6036 + 36 = 6072

1864 + 62 = 1926

8692 + 73 = 8765

ANSWERS

Maths Minute 34

Andrew Brodie Publications
© A & C Black Publishers Ltd.

◆ Name	● Name	▲ Name	✸ Name
Subtraction with 1 decimal place	Subtraction with 1 decimal place	Subtraction with 1 decimal place	Subtraction with 1 decimal place
$6.8 - 2.3 =$	$1.4 - 0.2 =$	$1.9 - 0.4 =$	$4.5 - 2.3 =$
$7.5 - 3.1 =$	$4.8 - 3.4 =$	$6.8 - 3.2 =$	$2.9 - 1.7 =$
$8.6 - 7.4 =$	$6.9 - 3.6 =$	$4.6 - 2.3 =$	$6.2 - 3.1 =$
$7.5 - 3.3 =$	$8.9 - 5.6 =$	$5.8 - 3.7 =$	$3.8 - 1.6 =$
$4.8 - 2.4 =$	$2.8 - 1.7 =$	$2.6 - 1.4 =$	$2.8 - 1.5 =$
$3.9 - 3.6 =$	$6.6 - 3.5 =$	$6.6 - 5.5 =$	$5.5 - 2.3 =$
$9.4 - 8.1 =$	$7.6 - 4.1 =$	$3.8 - 2.6 =$	$7.6 - 4.2 =$
$7.2 - 5.1 =$	$7.2 - 3.0 =$	$7.7 - 1.6 =$	$8.2 - 4.1 =$
$5.5 - 4.0 =$	$9.5 - 6.3 =$	$3.9 - 1.3 =$	$1.8 - 0.3 =$
$4.9 - 2.7 =$	$2.6 - 1.3 =$	$7.2 - 5.1 =$	$7.4 - 6.3 =$
$3.7 - 1.6 =$	$9.1 - 7.1 =$	$1.7 - 0.4 =$	$6.6 - 1.7 =$
$5.3 - 3.2 =$	$5.9 - 4.2 =$	$8.5 - 3.8 =$	$5.1 - 3.4 =$
$2.4 - 2.3 =$	$8.5 - 4.8 =$	$6.3 - 2.5 =$	$4.7 - 2.5 =$
$7.6 - 0.5 =$	$9.6 - 6.8 =$	$5.1 - 4.4 =$	$7.3 - 3.8 =$
$8.8 - 3.9 =$	$3.9 - 1.9 =$	$9.9 - 1.6 =$	$8.7 - 2.9 =$
$3.5 - 2.8 =$	$9.8 - 6.9 =$	$2.8 - 0.9 =$	$5.4 - 1.6 =$

Maths Minute 35

Andrew Brodie Publications
© A & C Black Publishers Ltd.

◆ ANSWERS

Subtraction with 1 decimal place

$6 \cdot 8 - 2 \cdot 3 = 4 \cdot 5$

$7 \cdot 5 - 3 \cdot 1 = 4 \cdot 4$

$8 \cdot 6 - 7 \cdot 4 = 1 \cdot 2$

$7 \cdot 5 - 3 \cdot 3 = 4 \cdot 2$

$4 \cdot 8 - 2 \cdot 4 = 2 \cdot 4$

$3 \cdot 9 - 3 \cdot 6 = 0 \cdot 3$

$9 \cdot 4 - 8 \cdot 1 = 1 \cdot 3$

$7 \cdot 2 - 5 \cdot 1 = 2 \cdot 1$

$5 \cdot 5 - 4 \cdot 0 = 1 \cdot 5$

$4 \cdot 9 - 2 \cdot 7 = 2 \cdot 2$

$3 \cdot 7 - 1 \cdot 6 = 2 \cdot 1$

$5 \cdot 3 - 3 \cdot 2 = 2 \cdot 1$

$2 \cdot 4 - 2 \cdot 3 = 0 \cdot 1$

$7 \cdot 6 - 0 \cdot 5 = 7 \cdot 1$

$8 \cdot 8 - 3 \cdot 9 = 4 \cdot 9$

$3 \cdot 5 - 2 \cdot 8 = 0 \cdot 7$

ANSWERS

Maths Minute 35

Andrew Brodie Publications
© A & C Black Publishers Ltd.

● ANSWERS

Subtraction with 1 decimal place

$1 \cdot 4 - 0 \cdot 2 = 1 \cdot 2$

$4 \cdot 8 - 3 \cdot 4 = 1 \cdot 4$

$6 \cdot 9 - 3 \cdot 6 = 3 \cdot 3$

$8 \cdot 9 - 5 \cdot 6 = 3 \cdot 3$

$2 \cdot 8 - 1 \cdot 7 = 1 \cdot 1$

$6 \cdot 6 - 3 \cdot 5 = 3 \cdot 1$

$7 \cdot 6 - 4 \cdot 1 = 3 \cdot 5$

$7 \cdot 2 - 3 \cdot 0 = 4 \cdot 2$

$9 \cdot 5 - 6 \cdot 3 = 3 \cdot 2$

$2 \cdot 6 - 1 \cdot 3 = 1 \cdot 3$

$9 \cdot 1 - 7 \cdot 1 = 2$

$5 \cdot 9 - 4 \cdot 2 = 1 \cdot 7$

$8 \cdot 5 - 4 \cdot 8 = 3 \cdot 7$

$9 \cdot 6 - 6 \cdot 8 = 2 \cdot 8$

$3 \cdot 9 - 1 \cdot 9 = 2$

$9 \cdot 8 - 6 \cdot 9 = 2 \cdot 9$

ANSWERS

Maths Minute 35

Andrew Brodie Publications
© A & C Black Publishers Ltd.

▲ ANSWERS

Subtraction with 1 decimal place

$1 \cdot 9 - 0 \cdot 4 = 1 \cdot 5$

$6 \cdot 8 - 3 \cdot 2 = 3 \cdot 6$

$4 \cdot 6 - 2 \cdot 3 = 2 \cdot 3$

$5 \cdot 8 - 3 \cdot 7 = 2 \cdot 1$

$2 \cdot 6 - 1 \cdot 4 = 1 \cdot 2$

$6 \cdot 6 - 5 \cdot 5 = 1 \cdot 1$

$3 \cdot 8 - 2 \cdot 6 = 1 \cdot 2$

$7 \cdot 7 - 1 \cdot 6 = 6 \cdot 1$

$3 \cdot 9 - 1 \cdot 3 = 2 \cdot 6$

$7 \cdot 2 - 5 \cdot 1 = 2 \cdot 1$

$1 \cdot 7 - 0 \cdot 4 = 1 \cdot 3$

$8 \cdot 5 - 3 \cdot 8 = 4 \cdot 7$

$6 \cdot 3 - 2 \cdot 5 = 3 \cdot 8$

$5 \cdot 1 - 4 \cdot 4 = 0 \cdot 7$

$9 \cdot 9 - 1 \cdot 6 = 8 \cdot 3$

$2 \cdot 8 - 0 \cdot 9 = 1 \cdot 9$

ANSWERS

Maths Minute 35

Andrew Brodie Publications
© A & C Black Publishers Ltd.

✳ ANSWERS

Subtraction with 1 decimal place

$4 \cdot 5 - 2 \cdot 3 = 2 \cdot 2$

$2 \cdot 9 - 1 \cdot 7 = 1 \cdot 2$

$6 \cdot 2 - 3 \cdot 1 = 3 \cdot 1$

$3 \cdot 8 - 1 \cdot 6 = 2 \cdot 2$

$2 \cdot 8 - 1 \cdot 5 = 1 \cdot 3$

$5 \cdot 5 - 2 \cdot 3 = 3 \cdot 2$

$7 \cdot 6 - 4 \cdot 2 = 3 \cdot 4$

$8 \cdot 2 - 4 \cdot 1 = 4 \cdot 1$

$1 \cdot 8 - 0 \cdot 3 = 1 \cdot 5$

$7 \cdot 4 - 6 \cdot 3 = 1 \cdot 1$

$6 \cdot 6 - 1 \cdot 7 = 4 \cdot 9$

$5 \cdot 1 - 3 \cdot 4 = 1 \cdot 7$

$4 \cdot 7 - 2 \cdot 5 = 2 \cdot 2$

$7 \cdot 3 - 3 \cdot 8 = 3 \cdot 5$

$8 \cdot 7 - 2 \cdot 9 = 5 \cdot 8$

$5 \cdot 4 - 1 \cdot 6 = 3 \cdot 8$

ANSWERS

Maths Minute 35

Andrew Brodie Publications
© A & C Black Publishers Ltd.

◆ Name	● Name	▲ Name	✴ Name
3 digit minus 3 digit numbers	3 digit minus 3 digit numbers	3 digit minus 3 digit numbers	3 digit minus 3 digit numbers
627 – 413 =	563 – 230 =	596 – 331 =	876 – 433 =
838 – 424 =	827 – 616 =	438 – 111 =	299 – 129 =
492 – 361 =	499 – 309 =	598 – 362 =	989 – 481 =
568 – 452 =	600 – 400 =	639 – 318 =	277 – 133 =
580 – 520 =	783 – 551 =	828 – 428 =	698 – 371 =
695 – 355 =	628 – 317 =	756 – 344 =	961 – 590 =
778 – 426 =	950 – 830 =	790 – 287 =	498 – 314 =
889 – 418 =	473 – 251 =	972 – 970 =	648 – 324 =
987 – 555 =	998 – 818 =	569 – 433 =	846 – 423 =
877 – 421 =	769 – 548 =	534 – 213 =	666 – 333 =
439 – 216 =	673 – 341 =	799 – 686 =	978 – 465 =
586 – 452 =	554 – 440 =	587 – 213 =	868 – 737 =

Maths Minute 36

Andrew Brodie Publications
© A & C Black Publishers Ltd.
Andrew Brodie Publications
© A & C Black Publishers Ltd.
Andrew Brodie Publications
© A & C Black Publishers Ltd.
Andrew Brodie Publications
© A & C Black Publishers Ltd.

◆ ANSWERS
3 digit minus 3 digit numbers

627 − 413 = 214

838 − 424 = 414

492 − 361 = 131

568 − 452 = 116

580 − 520 = 60

695 − 355 = 340

778 − 426 = 352

889 − 418 = 471

987 − 555 = 432

877 − 421 = 456

439 − 216 = 223

586 − 452 = 134

ANSWERS

Maths Minute 36

Andrew Brodie Publications
© A & C Black Publishers Ltd.

● ANSWERS
3 digit minus 3 digit numbers

563 − 230 = 333

827 − 616 = 211

499 − 309 = 190

600 − 400 = 200

783 − 551 = 232

628 − 317 = 311

950 − 830 = 120

473 − 251 = 222

998 − 818 = 180

769 − 548 = 221

673 − 341 = 332

554 − 440 = 114

ANSWERS

Maths Minute 36

Andrew Brodie Publications
© A & C Black Publishers Ltd.

▲ ANSWERS
3 digit minus 3 digit numbers

596 − 331 = 265

438 − 111 = 327

598 − 362 = 236

639 − 318 = 321

828 − 428 = 400

756 − 344 = 412

790 − 287 = 503

972 − 970 = 2

569 − 433 = 136

534 − 213 = 321

799 − 686 = 113

587 − 213 = 374

ANSWERS

Maths Minute 36

Andrew Brodie Publications
© A & C Black Publishers Ltd.

✷ ANSWERS
3 digit minus 3 digit numbers

876 − 433 = 443

299 − 129 = 170

989 − 481 = 508

277 − 133 = 144

698 − 371 = 327

961 − 590 = 371

498 − 314 = 184

648 − 324 = 324

846 − 423 = 423

666 − 333 = 333

978 − 465 = 513

868 − 737 = 131

ANSWERS

Maths Minute 36

Andrew Brodie Publications
© A & C Black Publishers Ltd.

◆ Name	● Name	▲ Name
4 digit add 3 digit numbers	4 digit add 3 digit numbers	4 digit add 3 digit numbers
2841 + 123 =	6704 + 165 =	5414 + 273 =
1881 + 101 =	2408 + 301 =	3203 + 364 =
4208 + 402 =	9888 + 111 =	2300 + 562 =
6124 + 321 =	1420 + 342 =	4911 + 144 =
3790 + 200 =	6920 + 178 =	5329 + 430 =
6312 + 516 =	3904 + 181 =	3941 + 100 =
5416 + 301 =	6784 + 115 =	6812 + 167 =
3520 + 459 =	4692 + 208 =	1329 + 330 =
9034 + 323 =	5400 + 392 =	8294 + 503 =
1763 + 146 =	1980 + 119 =	6846 + 122 =
2632 + 318 =	7481 + 218 =	2420 + 346 =
4391 + 506 =	2899 + 100 =	4224 + 741 =

Maths Minute 37

Andrew Brodie Publications
© A & C Black Publishers Ltd.

Maths Minute 37

Andrew Brodie Publications
© A & C Black Publishers Ltd.

Maths Minute 37

Andrew Brodie Publications
© A & C Black Publishers Ltd.

◆ ANSWERS

4 digit add 3 digit numbers

2841 + 123 = 2964

1881 + 101 = 1982

4208 + 402 = 4610

6124 + 321 = 6445

3790 + 200 = 3990

6312 + 516 = 6828

5416 + 301 = 5717

3520 + 459 = 3979

9034 + 323 = 9357

1763 + 146 = 1909

2632 + 318 = 2950

4391 + 506 = 4897

ANSWERS

Maths Minute 37

Andrew Brodie Publications
© A & C Black Publishers Ltd.

● ANSWERS

4 digit add 3 digit numbers

6704 + 165 = 6869

2408 + 301 = 2709

9888 + 111 = 9999

1420 + 342 = 1762

6920 + 178 = 7098

3904 + 181 = 4085

6784 + 115 = 6899

4692 + 208 = 4900

5400 + 392 = 5792

1980 + 119 = 2099

7481 + 218 = 7699

2899 + 100 = 2999

ANSWERS

Maths Minute 37

Andrew Brodie Publications
© A & C Black Publishers Ltd.

▲ ANSWERS

4 digit add 3 digit numbers

5414 + 273 = 5687

3203 + 364 = 3567

2300 + 562 = 2862

4911 + 144 = 5055

5329 + 430 = 5759

3941 + 100 = 4041

6812 + 167 = 6979

1329 + 330 = 1659

8294 + 503 = 8797

6846 + 122 = 6968

2420 + 346 = 2766

4224 + 741 = 4965

ANSWERS

Maths Minute 37

Andrew Brodie Publications
© A & C Black Publishers Ltd.

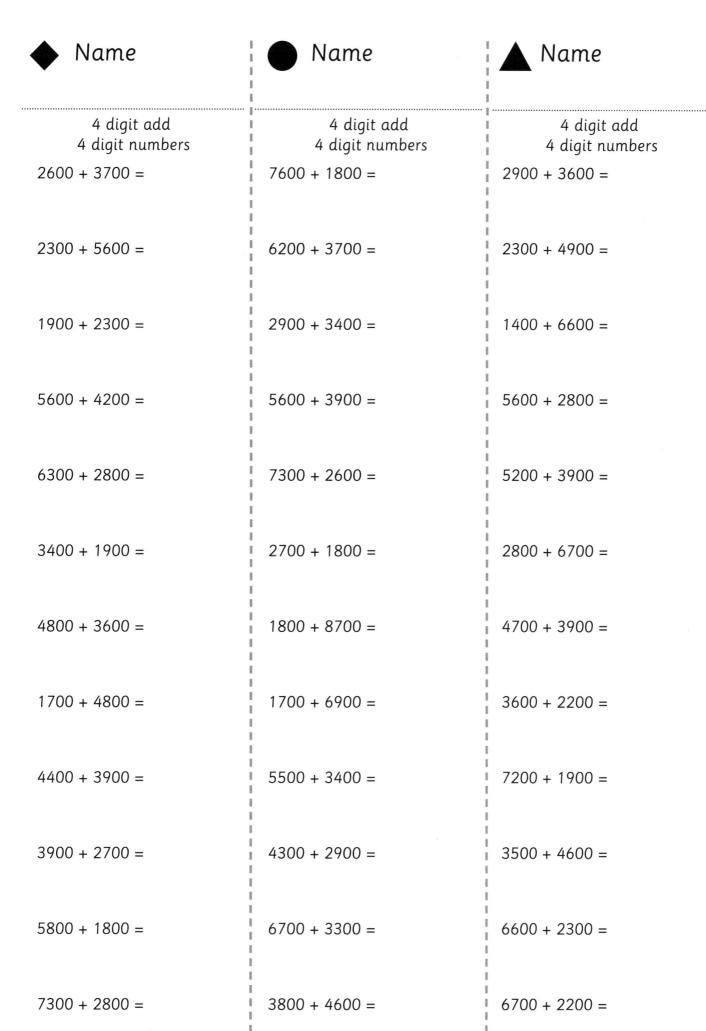

◆ Name	● Name	▲ Name
4 digit add 4 digit numbers	4 digit add 4 digit numbers	4 digit add 4 digit numbers
2600 + 3700 =	7600 + 1800 =	2900 + 3600 =
2300 + 5600 =	6200 + 3700 =	2300 + 4900 =
1900 + 2300 =	2900 + 3400 =	1400 + 6600 =
5600 + 4200 =	5600 + 3900 =	5600 + 2800 =
6300 + 2800 =	7300 + 2600 =	5200 + 3900 =
3400 + 1900 =	2700 + 1800 =	2800 + 6700 =
4800 + 3600 =	1800 + 8700 =	4700 + 3900 =
1700 + 4800 =	1700 + 6900 =	3600 + 2200 =
4400 + 3900 =	5500 + 3400 =	7200 + 1900 =
3900 + 2700 =	4300 + 2900 =	3500 + 4600 =
5800 + 1800 =	6700 + 3300 =	6600 + 2300 =
7300 + 2800 =	3800 + 4600 =	6700 + 2200 =

Maths Minute 38

Andrew Brodie Publications
© A & C Black Publishers Ltd.

Maths Minute 38

Andrew Brodie Publications
© A & C Black Publishers Ltd.

Maths Minute 38

Andrew Brodie Publications
© A & C Black Publishers Ltd.

2600 + 3700 = 6300

2300 + 5600 = 7900

1900 + 2300 = 4200

5600 + 4200 = 9800

6300 + 2800 = 9100

3400 + 1900 = 5300

4800 + 3600 = 8400

1700 + 4800 = 6500

4400 + 3900 = 8300

3900 + 2700 = 6600

5800 + 1800 = 7600

7300 + 2800 = 10100

ANSWERS

Maths Minute 38

Andrew Brodie Publications
© A & C Black Publishers Ltd.

7600 + 1800 = 9400

6200 + 3700 = 9900

2900 + 3400 = 6300

5600 + 3900 = 9500

7300 + 2600 = 9900

2700 + 1800 = 4500

1800 + 8700 = 10500

1700 + 6900 = 8600

5500 + 3400 = 8900

4300 + 2900 = 7200

6700 + 3300 = 10000

3800 + 4600 = 8400

ANSWERS

Maths Minute 38

Andrew Brodie Publications
© A & C Black Publishers Ltd.

2900 + 3600 = 6500

2300 + 4900 = 7200

1400 + 6600 = 8000

5600 + 2800 = 8400

5200 + 3900 = 9100

2800 + 6700 = 9500

4700 + 3900 = 8600

3600 + 2200 = 5800

7200 + 1900 = 9100

3500 + 4600 = 8100

6600 + 2300 = 8900

6700 + 2200 = 8900

ANSWERS

Maths Minute 38

Andrew Brodie Publications
© A & C Black Publishers Ltd.

◆ Name

● Name

▲ Name

Addition with 2
decimal places

Addition with 2
decimal places

Addition with 2
decimal places

0·25 + 0·25 =

0·35 + 0·25 =

0·25 + 0·75 =

0·35 + 0·5 =

0·26 + 0·13 =

0·55 + 0·22 =

0·71 + 0·6 =

0·05 + 0·22 =

0·75 + 0·05 =

0·55 + 0·5 =

0·95 + 0·12 =

0·16 + 0·5 =

0·67 + 0·3 =

0·04 + 0·91 =

0·93 + 0·1 =

0·26 + 0·8 =

0·46 + 0·32 =

0·48 + 0·3 =

0·12 + 0·5 =

0·64 + 0·76 =

0·96 + 0·6 =

0·48 + 0·11 =

0·17 + 0·81 =

0·15 + 0·15 =

0·75 + 0·32 =

0·15 + 0·59 =

0·5 + 0·45 =

0·5 + 0·5 =

0·82 + 0·88 =

0·85 + 0·26 =

0·3 + 0·3 =

0·93 + 0·1 =

0·42 + 0·83 =

0·15 + 0·26 =

0·19 + 0·6 =

0·72 + 0·62 =

Maths Minute 39

Maths Minute 39

Maths Minute 39

Andrew Brodie Publications
© A & C Black Publishers Ltd.

Andrew Brodie Publications
© A & C Black Publishers Ltd.

Andrew Brodie Publications
© A & C Black Publishers Ltd.

0·25 + 0·25 = 0·5

0·35 + 0·5 = 0·85

0·71 + 0·6 = 1·31

0·55 + 0·5 = 1·05

0·67 + 0·3 = 0·97

0·26 + 0·8 = 1·06

0·12 + 0·5 = 0·62

0·48 + 0·11 = 0·59

0·75 + 0·32 = 1·07

0·5 + 0·5 = 1

0·3 + 0·3 = 0·6

0·15 + 0·26 = 0·41

ANSWERS

Maths Minute 39

Andrew Brodie Publications
© A & C Black Publishers Ltd.

0·35 + 0·25 = 0·6

0·26 + 0·13 = 0·39

0·05 + 0·22 = 0·27

0·95 + 0·12 = 1·07

0·04 + 0·91 = 0·95

0·46 + 0·32 = 0·78

0·64 + 0·76 = 1·4

0·17 + 0·81 = 0·98

0·15 + 0·59 = 0·74

0·82 + 0·88 = 1·7

0·93 + 0·1 = 1·03

0·19 + 0·6 = 0·79

ANSWERS

Maths Minute 39

Andrew Brodie Publications
© A & C Black Publishers Ltd.

0·25 + 0·75 = 1

0·55 + 0·22 = 0·77

0·75 + 0·05 = 0·8

0·16 + 0·5 = 0·66

0·93 + 0·1 = 1·03

0·48 + 0·3 = 0·78

0·96 + 0·6 = 1·56

0·15 + 0·15 = 0·3

0·5 + 0·45 = 0·95

0·85 + 0·26 = 1·11

0·42 + 0·83 = 1·25

0·72 + 0·62 = 1·34

ANSWERS

Maths Minute 39

Andrew Brodie Publications
© A & C Black Publishers Ltd.

◆ Name	● Name	▲ Name

Mixture | Mixture | Mixture

◆	●	▲
50% of 50 =	50% of 82 =	50% of 246 =
50% of 48 =	50% of 46 =	50% of 410 =
50% of 36 =	50% of 268 =	50% of 78 =
50% of 68 =	50% of 282 =	50% of 56 =
25% of 12 =	25% of 24 =	25% of 48 =
25% of 20 =	25% of 36 =	25% of 52 =
25% of 16 =	25% of 28 =	25% of 152 =
25% of 40 =	25% of 80 =	25% of 252 =
$\frac{1}{5}$ of 40 =	$\frac{1}{5}$ of 55 =	$\frac{1}{5}$ of 85 =
$\frac{1}{5}$ of 25 =	$\frac{1}{5}$ of 30 =	$\frac{1}{5}$ of 70 =
$\frac{1}{5}$ of 45 =	$\frac{1}{5}$ of 75 =	$\frac{2}{5}$ of 10 =
$\frac{1}{5}$ of 90 =	$\frac{1}{5}$ of 60 =	$\frac{2}{5}$ of 20 =
231 + 132 =	349 + 440 =	553 + 442 =
181 + 107 =	460 + 239 =	581 + 118 =
262 + 106 =	306 + 483 =	626 + 312 =
754 + 123 =	421 + 136 =	632 + 167 =
2900 + 3600 =	5400 + 1700 =	4900 + 3800 =
5600 + 3200 =	3800 + 2900 =	6300 + 2700 =
1400 + 8600 =	3200 + 1400 =	7100 + 2600 =
6700 + 2800 =	4100 + 2900 =	2700 + 2700 =
0·35 + 0·15 =	0·95 + 0·18 =	0·76 + 0·6 =
0·75 + 0·25 =	0·15 + 0·25 =	0·11 + 0·9 =
0·26 + 0·26 =	0·63 + 0·5 =	0·81 + 0·2 =
0·72 + 0·32 =	0·37 + 0·7 =	0·5 + 0·6 =

Maths Minute 40

Andrew Brodie Publications
© A & C Black Publishers Ltd.

Maths Minute 40

Andrew Brodie Publications
© A & C Black Publishers Ltd.

Maths Minute 40

Andrew Brodie Publications
© A & C Black Publishers Ltd.

◆ ANSWERS
Mixture

50% of 50 = 25

50% of 48 = 24

50% of 36 = 18

50% of 68 = 34

25% of 12 =   3

25% of 20 =   5

25% of 16 =   4

25% of 40 = 10

$\frac{1}{5}$ of 40 =   8

$\frac{1}{5}$ of 25 =   5

$\frac{1}{5}$ of 45 =   9

$\frac{1}{5}$ of 90 = 18

231 + 132 = 363

181 + 107 = 288

262 + 106 = 368

754 + 123 = 877

2900 + 3600 = 6500

5600 + 3200 = 8800

1400 + 8600 = 10000

6700 + 2800 = 9500

0·35 + 0·15 = 0·5

0·75 + 0·25 = 1

0·26 + 0·26 = 0·52

0·72 + 0·32 = 1·04

ANSWERS
Maths Minute 40
Andrew Brodie Publications
© A & C Black Publishers Ltd.

● ANSWERS
Mixture

50% of 82 = 41

50% of 46 = 23

50% of 268 = 134

50% of 282 = 141

25% of 24 =   6

25% of 36 =   9

25% of 28 =   7

25% of 80 = 20

$\frac{1}{5}$ of 55 = 11

$\frac{1}{5}$ of 30 =   6

$\frac{1}{5}$ of 75 = 15

$\frac{1}{5}$ of 60 = 12

349 + 440 = 489

460 + 239 = 699

306 + 483 = 789

421 + 136 = 557

5400 + 1700 = 7100

3800 + 2900 = 6700

3200 + 1400 = 4600

4100 + 2900 = 7000

0·95 + 0·18 = 1·13

0·15 + 0·25 = 0·4

0·63 + 0·5 = 1·13

0·37 + 0·7 = 1·07

ANSWERS
Maths Minute 40
Andrew Brodie Publications
© A & C Black Publishers Ltd.

▲ ANSWERS
Mixture

50% of 246 = 123

50% of 410 = 205

50% of 78 = 39

50% of 56 = 28

25% of 48 = 12

25% of 52 = 13

25% of 152 = 38

25% of 252 = 63

$\frac{1}{5}$ of 85 = 17

$\frac{1}{5}$ of 70 = 14

$\frac{2}{5}$ of 10 =   4

$\frac{2}{5}$ of 20 =   8

553 + 442 = 995

581 + 118 = 699

626 + 312 = 938

632 + 167 = 799

4900 + 3800 = 8700

6300 + 2700 = 9000

7100 + 2600 = 9700

2700 + 2700 = 5400

0·76 + 0·6 = 1·36

0·11 + 0·9 = 1·01

0·81 + 0·2 = 1·01

0·5 + 0·6 = 1·10

ANSWERS
Maths Minute 40
Andrew Brodie Publications
© A & C Black Publishers Ltd.